MED-SURG NCLEX-RN REVIEW:

424 Exam Practice Questions with Detailed Rationales Explaining Correct and Incorrect Answer Choices

NurseEdu.com

Disclaimer:

Although the author and publisher have made every effort to ensure that the information in this book was correct at press time, the author and publisher do not assume and hereby disclaim any liability to any party for any loss, damage, or disruption caused by errors or omissions, whether such errors or omissions result from negligence, accident, or any other cause.

This book is not intended as a substitute for the medical advice of physicians. The reader should regularly consult a physician in matters relating to their health and particularly with respect to any symptoms that may require diagnosis or medical attention.

NCLEX®, NCLEX®-RN, and NCLEX®-PN are registered trademarks of the National Council of State Boards of Nursing, Inc. They hold no affiliation with this product.

Some images within this book are either royalty-free images, used under license from their respective copyright holders, or images that are in the public domain.

ISBN: 978-1-952914-07-2

FREE BONUS

FREE Download – Just Visit:

NurseEdu.com/bonus

TABLE OF CONTENTS

NCLEX-RN – MED-SURG: CARDIOVASCULAR – 40 QUESTIONS

1. A patient is admitted to the emergency room with a myocardial infarction. The patient's blood pressure is 80/40 mmHg. Upon assessing the patient, what should the nurse expect to find as an early assessment for this patient?

   A. Heart rate 130 bpm
   B. Troponin I 0.02 ng/mL
   C. Right arm pain
   D. Respiratory rate at 10 bpm

Rationale:

Correct answer: A

A myocardial infarction occurs when a coronary artery is blocked. This reduces the oxygenated blood supply to a portion of the myocardium (heart muscle). The affected muscle starts to infarct, or die, decreasing its ability to contract. This leads to decreased cardiac output. Typical signs and symptoms include hypotension, tachycardia, decreased oxygen saturation, chest pain, shortness of breath, left arm pain and numbness, nausea, vomiting, and anxiety.

A is correct because when blood pressure is decreased, baroreceptors in the aortic arch sense the decreased pressure within the vessels. In response, the parasympathetic system lessens sinoatrial node inhibition, thereby increasing heart rate as well as respiratory rate. Tachycardia is an early sign that begins before blood pressure is critically low. The heart is beating faster as a compensatory mechanism.

B is incorrect because it is a normal Troponin I level. The nurse would expect to see increased Troponin I within 4 to 6 hours after the myocardial infarction.

C is incorrect because left arm pain is a common symptom in patients experiencing an MI, not right arm pain. The nerves that supply the heart and the left arm are from the same spinal segment. The pain originates from the left chest (since the heart is slightly tilted left) and can radiate to the left arm, left nape of the neck, and left jaw.

D is incorrect because increased respirations occur as part of the compensation process, not decreased respirations.

2. A patient is given a beta blocker according to the healthcare provider's orders. When the nurse assesses the patient later, which findings should be expected?

    A. Blood pressure change from 100/40 mmHg to 140/80 mmHg
    B. Respiratory rate change from 24 bpm to 16 bpm
    C. Oxygen saturation level change from 86% to 98%
    D. Pulse rate change from 110 bpm to 76 bpm

Rationale:

Correct answer: D

Beta blockers are administered to block stimulation of beta-1 000. This blocks sympathetic response, which decreases the heart rate as well as blood pressure. Ventricular filling time is increased due to the decrease in heart rate.

A is incorrect because beta blockers will decrease the heart rate causing decreased cardiac output and decreased blood pressure. These medications do not generally cause hypertension. On the contrary, they are used to treat hypertension.

B is incorrect because there is usually no effect on beta-2 adrenergic receptor sites or respiratory status.

C is incorrect because there is usually no effect on beta-2 adrenergic receptor sites or respiratory status. An increase in SpO_2 is a good outcome for the patient, but it is not a direct action of beta-blockers.

3. The nurse on the medical-surgical floor is assessing patients. Which of the following patients is at greatest risk for cardiovascular disease?

    A. 74-year-old woman admitted for asthma exacerbation

B. 66-year-old man, recently immigrated from Japan, admitted for colon cancer

C. 53-year-old African American man admitted for diabetes mellitus

D. 62-year-old postmenopausal woman taking hormone therapy

Rationale:

Correct answer: C

Coronary artery disease and hypertension are more prevalent in American Indians than whites and Asian Americans. Risk of hypertension and coronary artery disease is increased with diabetes mellitus patients. African Americans and males are also at higher risk for cardiovascular disease. So, this patient has two risk factors. Modifiable risk factors include hypertension, tobacco use, physical inactivity, hyperlipidemia, and overweight/obesity.

A is incorrect because asthma does not lead to increased risk of cardiovascular disease. This patient has one risk factor: increased age. Men are more at risk for cardiovascular disease than premenopausal women.

B is incorrect because colon cancer does not lead to increased risk of cardiovascular disease. This patient has no risk factors. Immigrants from eastern Asian countries are at less risk for cardiovascular disease. Their children and grandchildren, however, typically have increased risk for cardiovascular disease than the original immigrants due to adopting the western lifestyle.

D is incorrect because hormone therapy does not increase risk of cardiovascular disease. The risk for cardiovascular disease increases after women reach menopause. So, this patient has one risk factor.

4. The nurse is assessing a 65-year-old patient with several chronic diseases. The patient's heart rate is noted to be 47 bpm. What is the first action the nurse should take?

A. Document the finding

B. Prepare to externally pace the patient

C. Review medications in the patient's chart

D. Administer 1 mg of atropine

Rationale:

Correct answer: C

The conduction system of the heart is made up of pacemaker cells, which decrease in number as we age and can cause bradycardia. Medication reconciliation should be checked first to identify medications that decrease heart rate, then the healthcare provider should be informed.

A is incorrect because documentation must be performed, but not as a priority. The nurse should care for the patient first and document when care has been completed.

B is incorrect because external pacing is not indicated for this patient.

D is incorrect because although atropine may be indicated for treatment of bradycardia, the nurse should first check the medication to determine if the patient takes anything that can cause the decreased heart rate.

5. The nurse obtains a health history from a patient in the emergency room. Which of the following statements made by the patient could indicate heart failure?

    A. "Climbing stairs makes me short of breath."
    B. "I can see halos floating above my head."
    C. "My memory is troubling me these days."
    D. "I've lost several pounds over the last few weeks."

Rationale:

Correct answer: A

An early manifestation of heart failure includes dyspnea upon exertion, such as climbing stairs. Other symptoms include peripheral edema, decreased cardiac output and blood pressure, irregular cardiac rhythm or palpitations, fatigue, and cough.

B is incorrect because halos in the line of sight are not specific to early signs of heart failure. Halos can indicate glaucoma or cataracts. Visual halos can be an adverse effect of digoxin.

C is incorrect because memory trouble is not specific to early signs of heart failure.

D is incorrect because loss of weight is not specific to early signs of heart failure.

6. The nurse is obtaining the health history of a new patient on the medical floor. Which patient statement should alert the nurse to the presence of edema?

A. "I have to get up at night to go to the bathroom."

B. "By the end of the day I have to take off my shoes; they're so tight."

C. "My wedding ring keeps slipping off my finger."

D. "My intake includes 18 glasses of water daily."

Rationale:

Correct answer: B

Fluid accumulation within interstitial spaces, also known as edema, can cause weight gain. Fit of shoes and rings for tightness should be noted, as well as any indentations in the legs from socks.

A is incorrect because nighttime bathroom trips are not indicative of edema.

C is incorrect because edema will often cause the fingers to swell, making it harder to get rings on and off.

D is incorrect because increased water intake is not necessarily indicative of edema, (although it may cause peripheral fluid retention). This patient is taking in more than the recommended amount of daily fluid. This statement needs to be investigated further by the nurse. Increased fluid intake can lead to fluid volume overload.

7. The nurse is assessing a 75-year-old patient. Which of the following assessments will cause the nurse to suspect a myocardial infarction?

A. Complaint of chest pain with inspiration

B. Complaint of weakness in the left arm and hand

C. Confusion and disorientation

D. Complaint of pounding headache

Rationale:

Correct answer: C

Myocardial infarction can cause decreased cardiac output, resulting in decreased cerebral blood supply. This can lead to confusion and disorientation, especially in older adults.

A is incorrect because chest pain on inspiration is an indication of pleurisy, not MI. Pleurisy (also known as pleuritis) is inflammation of the pleural lining of the lungs and the thoracic cavity.

B is incorrect because unilateral weakness and difficulty with fine motor control can be a sign of a stroke, not MI. MI can cause pain in the left arm, neck, and jaw but not weakness.

D is incorrect because myocardial infarction does not often cause a severe headache. Common symptoms include shortness of breath, nausea, feeling faint, cold sweats, and lethargy.

8. A patient is recovering from cardiac angiography with left femoral artery access. When assessing the patient's left foot, the nurse determines the pedal pulse is weak. What is the first action the nurse should take?

    A. Bend the left leg slightly and apply sandbag pressure to the femoral access site
    B. Increase the patient's IV fluid rate
    C. Assess the left leg for color and temperature
    D. Document left pedal pulse 1+/4

Rationale:

Correct answer: C

Pulse loss distal to access site for angiography could indicate an arterial obstruction or hemorrhage. The nurse should assess both lower extremities and compare pulses. The nurse should also compare pulses to the pre-procedure assessment. Decreased pulse, cyanosis, pallor, and cool skin indicate decreased circulation. The healthcare provider should be notified once peripheral and vascular assessments are performed and data obtained.

A is incorrect because the leg should remain straight. Sandbag pressure (or a pressure dressing) must be applied for 4-6 hours post procedure to prevent bleeding or hematoma to the site.

B is incorrect because increasing the rate of IV fluid infusion is not indicated at this time. If hemorrhage is identified, IV fluids will be needed, but the nurse must complete the assessment before addressing fluid replacement needs.

D is incorrect because documentation of findings without notifying the healthcare provider is inappropriate.

9. A patient recovering from left-sided cardiac catheterization is assessed by the nurse. Immediate intervention is required for which of the following findings?

   A. Intake exceeds output
   B. Bruising at the access site
   C. Confusion
   D. Pain at the access site

Rationale:

Correct answer: C

Cerebral vascular accident (CVA) is a specific risk of left-sided cardiac catheterization. Changes in neurologic status require immediate action.

A is incorrect because although the dye used during cardiac catheterization can affect kidney function, causing decreased urine output, this is not the greatest concern. The confusion related to hemorrhage or CVA is the nurse's priority at this time.

B is incorrect because bruising at the access site is expected.

- Note: The patient should have a sterile dressing over the access site and the nurse does not remove the dressing to check for bruising. The doctor removes the dressing for the first time, and then the nurse can remove subsequent dressings as needed for dressing changes.

D is incorrect because pain at the access site is expected.

10. The nurse is preparing a patient scheduled for cardiac catheterization. Which of the following is the priority for the nurse before the catheterization?

   A. Assess anxiety level of the patient
   B. Incentive spirometry education
   C. Heart rate and rhythm
   D. Iodine based agent allergies

Rationale:

Correct answer: D

Allergy to iodine agents must be documented prior to cardiac catheterization as the contrast used for the procedure is based in iodine. A life-threatening allergic reaction can occur, making it high-priority.

A is incorrect because anxiety is a psychosocial assessment. It is more important for the nurse to assess for physical complications or contraindications related to the procedure.

B is incorrect because although it is important for the nurse to teach incentive spirometry, this is preventative treatment. Assessing for allergies is more important. If the patient does have an allergy to the dye, that would pose more of an actual problem than potential atelectasis related to immobility after the catheterization.

C is incorrect because obtaining a baseline cardiac status prior to the procedure is important, but not as important as assessing for allergies. If this patient is allergic to iodine, the catheterization procedure may need to be canceled or performed without contrast.

11. The nurse is preparing a patient for a magnetic resonance imaging (MRI) of the heart. The patient has a pacemaker due to a previous myocardial infarction. What action should be taken by the nurse?

    A. Obtain an ECG prior to the MRI
    B. Notify the healthcare provider before the MRI is scheduled
    C. Draw cardiac enzymes prior to the MRI
    D. Encourage the patient to drink more fluids before the MRI

Rationale:

Correct answer: B

In the past, MRI was contraindicated in all patients with implanted cardiac devices. Due to the magnetic field used in the MRI procedure, the pacemaker can be deactivated, device components can be damaged, and rapid pacing can be triggered. The MRI can also cause inappropriate shocks, burning the skin over the pacemaker implantation site. The healthcare provider should be notified of the patient's pacemaker so another diagnostic test can be ordered. MRI is only used with patients who have pacemakers when other alternative radiologic tests have been unsuccessful in making a diagnosis.

A is incorrect because an ECG prior to the MRI is not necessarily indicated.

C is incorrect because cardiac enzymes are not necessarily indicated.

D is incorrect because increased fluids are not indicated for this patient. The patient does not need to be NPO prior to the procedure either, but increased fluids are not a requirement.

12. A patient admitted to the medical unit for myocardial infarction has a pulmonary artery pressure of 24/13 mmHg. What is the first action the nurse should take?

    A. Compare current pressure to previous readings
    B. Increase IV fluid infusion rate
    C. Notify the healthcare provider immediately
    D. Document the pressure in the patient's chart

Rationale:

Correct answer: A

PA pressures are obtained through use of a pulmonary artery catheter or Swan-Ganz catheter. This number indicates pressure within the pulmonary artery. Normal PA pressure is between 15-26 mmHg systolic and 5-15 mmHg diastolic. This patient's pressure is normal, but the nurse is responsible for assessing for trends, which may indicate the need for intervention.

B is incorrect because IV fluids do not need to be increased for normal PA pressures. Low PA pressure can indicate fluid volume depletion, thus indicating the need for a higher rate of IV fluid infusion.

C is incorrect because the healthcare provider does not need to be notified of normal PA pressures. The nurse will notify the healthcare provider if the PA pressure drops or increases significantly.

D is incorrect because PA pressures should be documented after comparison to previous readings.

13. The nurse cares for a patient with 80% blockage of the right coronary artery (RCA). The patient is awaiting coronary bypass surgery. Which pre-operative intervention should the nurse be prepared to implement?

A. IV furosemide administration

B. External pacemaker

C. Endotracheal intubation

D. Central venous catheter placement

Rationale:

Correct answer: B

The RCA is the supplier for the right atrium and ventricle, inferior left ventricle, and AV node. In 50% of people, the RCA also supplies blood to the SA node. When the RCA is completely (or nearly completely) occluded, the conduction system of the heart is affected, leading to heart block necessitating external pacing in an emergency.

A is incorrect because furosemide will have no effect on AV or SA node stimulation.

C is incorrect because endotracheal intubation is not indicated for this patient pre-operatively. The anesthesia team will intubate and connect to mechanical ventilation during the OR procedure.

D is incorrect because central venous catheter access will not help stimulate AV or SA node electrical activity.

14. A patient with diabetes has a body mass index of 42 and is at high risk for coronary artery disease. Which nutrition-related statement should the nurse include in the patient's teaching?

    A. "A low-carbohydrate, high-protein diet is the best method for weight loss."

    B. "Weight loss and consuming necessary nutrients should be balanced."

    C. "I will have the nutritionist come and talk to you about heart-healthy dietary measures."

    D. "If you increase your exercise to five times per week, fewer dietary modifications will be needed."

Rationale:

Correct answer: B

The American Heart Association dietary guidelines should be followed by patients who are at risk for cardiovascular disease. The nurse should encourage consumption of vegetables and fruits, unrefined whole-grain, and fat-free dairy during weight loss. The nurse can include the following tips when teaching about a heart-healthy diet:

- Control portion sizes (a serving of pasta is ½ cup, a serving of meat is 2-3 oz)
- Limit unhealthy fats: less than 14 g saturated fat daily and less than 2 g trans fat daily (for people on a 2,000 calorie/daily diet)
- Drink at least eight glasses of water daily

A is incorrect because high-protein low-carb diets are usually high in calories and fat, which is unhealthy for people at risk for cardiovascular disease.

C is incorrect because the nurse needs to address the patient's risks. While it is acceptable to consult with the nutritionist, the nurse should first address the patient's needs directly, to avoid "passing the buck."

D is incorrect because together, a healthy diet and exercise are integral for reducing risk for cardiovascular disease. Increased exercise does not, alone, compensate for an unhealthy diet.

15. A patient with advanced cardiac disease tells the nurse she has difficulty sleeping at night. What is the best response by the nurse?

    A. "I will notify the healthcare provider so a sleep study can be ordered to determine the problem."
    B. "While sleeping, you are hypoxic, so we will provide you with a nasal cannula with oxygen to use at home."
    C. "A continuous positive airway pressure (CPAP) mask can help you breathe while you are sleeping."
    D. "Elevate your head with pillows while you sleep."

Rationale:

Correct answer: D

Orthopnea (shortness of breath due to lying flat) is likely being experienced by this patient. The patient should be taught by the nurse to raise their head and chest with a pillow(s) or use a recliner to sleep.

A is incorrect because it is not necessary to order polysomnography (sleep study) to identify the problem for this patient. This test measures brain activity, oxygen saturation, heart rate, breathing, and eye/leg movements. It is commonly used to diagnose sleep disorders.

B is incorrect because orthopnea is not relieved with oxygen therapy.

C is incorrect because orthopnea is not relieved with CPAP. A CPAP device is used to relieve obstructive sleep apnea. This machine increases airway pressure upon inhalation so the throat doesn't collapse while lying down.

16. A 52-year-old man patient recovering from myocardial infarction tells the nurse, "I probably need to eat less chili to prevent the return of that awful indigestion pain that brought me in here." What is the best response by the nurse?

    A. "It's a good idea to cut chili out of your diet because it is high in calories and fat."
    B. "You now have an antacid prescribed that you will take each morning."
    C. "Tell me what you understand about what happened."
    D. "When did this indigestion start?"

Rationale:

Correct answer: C

After a patient suffers an extreme life-threatening event such as a myocardial infarction, they may exhibit defense mechanisms as a way of protecting themself from the actual anxiety they are feeling about the experience. This patient is likely in denial about what happened to them. Denial is a defense mechanism in which a patient fails to acknowledge a particular thought, feeling, or experience. The nurse should ask the patient about their understanding of what happened and what it means to them, as a way of beginning a therapeutic conversation in which the patient can be presented with the facts related to what they experienced.

A is incorrect because it does not assess the patient's knowledge regarding the experience, nor does it help address the MI.

B is incorrect because it does not address the patient's knowledge regarding the experience, nor does it help address the MI. The patient may be started on an antacid if they experience gastro-esophageal reflux, but this is not directly related to an MI.

D is incorrect because it is a closed-ended question which will only give the nurse one piece of information. This is an appropriate question to ask at some point, but it does not address the denial indicated by the patient's statement.

17. The nurse cares for a patient being prepared for coronary artery bypass graft surgery. The patient tells the nurse, "I am afraid of potential complications after the procedure. I am not sure I want to follow through with this." What is the best response by the nurse?

    A. "The risk of complications with this surgery is relatively low."
    B. "Can I call the chaplain for you to speak with before the surgery?"
    C. "What are your concerns regarding the surgery?"
    D. "You will need assistance after the surgery. Tell me about your support system."

Rationale:

Correct answer: C

Coronary artery bypass grafting (CABG) is a complex surgery that improves blood flow to the heart. Potential complications include wound infection, bleeding, reaction to anesthesia, heart attack, stroke, and even death. The procedure requires general anesthesia, excision of a vein from the leg or chest wall, and placement of the excised vein over the blocked coronary artery to restore blood flow to the myocardium. The patient's concerns and feelings related to the surgery should be discussed with the nurse. The nurse is capable of clarifying concerns related to common procedures and surgeries. After the nurse addresses concerns, the healthcare provider may need to be called.

A is incorrect because this is an untrue statement and provides false reassurance. The nurse must address the patient's concerns. Even after the consent form has been signed, the patient legally still has the right to change their mind.

B is incorrect because the concerns of the patient should not be directed to the chaplain, as this is "passing the buck." The nurse should address the patient directly before consulting another member of the healthcare team.

D is incorrect because this dismisses the patient's current concerns. After the nurse addresses the fear and the complications, then support systems can be discussed.

18. The nurse in the emergency department is triaging four patients who have presented with chest discomfort. Which patient should be assessed by the nurse first?

    A. 45-year-old female, describes her pain as an "aching dullness" with numbness of the fingers
    B. 50-year-old male in moderate pain that increases with inspiration
    C. 54-year-old female whose pain is described as substernal radiating to the abdomen
    D. 60-year-old male whose pain is described as intense stabbing spreading across the chest

Rationale:

Correct answer: D

All patients complaining of chest pain must have a thorough assessment. In order to determine which patient must be seen first, common differences in descriptions of pain must be understood. Stabbing, squeezing pain that spreads across the chest, arms, jaw, back, or neck indicates a possible myocardial infarction. This patient should be seen by the nurse first.

A is incorrect because aching dullness and numb fingers is usually anxiety related.

B is incorrect because pain that worsens upon inspiration is usually a pleuropulmonary issue such as pleuritis (infection or inflammation of the lining of the lungs and thoracic cavity).

C is incorrect because pain radiating to the abdomen could be an esophageal or gastric issue, especially when experienced by a male patient. This type of pain could be myocardial related when experienced by a female patient. All these patients should be seen, but the patient complaining of stabbing pain spreading across the chest is the highest priority.

19. Which statement by the patient in an outpatient clinic would cause the nurse suspect left-sided heart failure?

    A. "I've drank more water lately than I usually do."
    B. "I have to get up at night to urinate."
    C. "When taking the stairs, I have to stop halfway and catch my breath."
    D. "Several times my vision has been blurry."

Rationale:

Correct answer: C

Left-sided heart failure, also known as left-ventricular heart failure, is the failure of the left ventricle to maintain a normal output of blood. The left ventricle does not empty completely, therefore, it cannot accept the full volume of blood returning from the lungs via the left atrium. This causes engorgement of the pulmonary veins, and fluid seeps out of these vessels into the tissues of the lungs, causing pulmonary edema. Patients report fatigue or weakness while performing activities of daily living when experiencing left-sided heart failure. They may also experience coughing and difficulty breathing or feel the need to "catch their breath" due to fluid moving into the alveoli.

A is incorrect because water intake and thirst are not indicative of left-sided heart failure. This statement by the patient indicates a need for investigation, however. Increased fluid intake could potentially cause fluid volume overload.

B is incorrect because nocturia or having to urinate at night is often experienced by patients with right-sided heart failure. Other symptoms include dependent edema, liver enlargement, bloating, abdominal tenderness, coolness of extremities, and weight gain.

D is incorrect because heart failure is not characterized by blurry vision.

20. A patient on the cardiac unit is assessed by the nurse. Which patient statement would cause the nurse to suspect right-sided heart failure?

    A. "I have four pillows under my head when I sleep."
    B. "My shoes have been so tight lately."
    C. "Every night I wake up coughing."
    D. "I have a hard time catching my breath lately."

Rationale:

Correct answer: B

Systemic congestion is a sign of right-sided heart failure. Fluid retention causes a build-up of pressure in the venous system, which leads to peripheral edema. This is due to the decreased ability of the heart to pump blood effectively in right-sided heart failure. Other symptoms include dependent edema, liver enlargement, bloating, abdominal tenderness, coolness of extremities, and weight gain. Treatment includes digoxin, antihypertensives, low-sodium diet, and diuretics.

A is incorrect because respiratory symptoms including paroxysmal nocturnal dyspnea and orthopnea are seen in left-sided heart failure. In this condition, the left ventricle fails to maintain a normal output of blood, leading to pulmonary edema.

C is incorrect because coughing is related to left-sided heart failure due to fluid accumulation in the lung tissue.

D is incorrect because difficulty breathing could be related to left-sided heart failure.

21. A patient on the cardiac unit is assessed by the nurse. When an S3 gallop is noted, what is the next action the nurse should take?

    A. Assess for symptoms of left-sided heart failure
    B. Document the S3 gallop as a normal finding
    C. Notify the healthcare provider immediately
    D. Arrange to transfer the patient to intensive care

Rationale:

Correct answer: A

Typical heart sounds are noted as S1 and S2. If there is a third heart sound, it is called S3, or S3 gallop. This is typically caused by blood flow suddenly slowing as it flows from the left atrium into the left ventricle. Early diastolic filling is indicated by S3 gallop and signifies increasing left ventricular pressure as well as left ventricular failure.

B is incorrect because an S3 gallop is an abnormal finding. Any abnormal finding should be a concern to the nurse. Appropriate nursing actions are to further assess or perform an appropriate nursing intervention if no further assessment data is warranted.

C is incorrect because the healthcare provider should be notified once the full assessment is completed. The healthcare provider is called when the nurse has enough assessment information or in a case of a medical emergency.

D is incorrect because a full assessment should be completed to see if a higher level of care is warranted. Transferring this patient to ICU without further assessment is "passing the buck."

22. A patient diagnosed with right-sided heart failure asks why daily weights are important. What is the best response by the nurse?

    A. "Daily weights are the best indicator of fluid loss or gain."
    B. "Daily weights will tell us if you're eating a healthy diet."
    C. "Hospital protocol requires daily weights of all inpatients."
    D. "Daily weights help you lose weight which can decrease heart failure incidence."

Rationale:

Correct answer: A

Fluid loss or gain is indicated by daily weights, which should be documented daily with heart failure patients. 2.2 pounds equals 1 liter of fluid. This excess fluid typically collects in the periphery in right-sided heart failure and is seen as edema in the legs and arms. The other responses by the nurse do not address the importance of fluid monitoring.

B is incorrect because daily weights do not necessarily indicate a healthy diet.

C is incorrect because it does not appropriately answer the patient's question. This may be a true statement, but it doesn't address the situation in the question.

D is incorrect because weight loss is not the goal for this patient.

23. A patient with heart failure has a new prescription for enalapril (Vasotec), and the nurse is performing teaching. Which statement should be included by the nurse for this patient's teaching?

    A. "You need to avoid using salt substitutes."
    B. "Take this medication with food."
    C. "Avoid using products containing aspirin."
    D. "You must check your pulse every day before taking the medication."

Rationale:

Correct answer: A

Angiotensin-converting enzyme (ACE) inhibitors including enalapril inhibit excretion of potassium, which can lead to hyperkalemia. This can be a life-threatening situation, so patients must be taught to limit their potassium intake. Salt substitutes contain potassium chloride and can further lead to increased serum levels of potassium.

B is incorrect because ACE inhibitors do not have to be taken with food.

C is incorrect because aspirin is not contraindicated when taking ACE inhibitors and is often prescribed in conjunction. Remember: aspirin should not be administered to patients with risk for bleeding or those who have clotting disorders. Aspirin is also contraindicated in patients under 21 years of age due to the risk of Reye's syndrome.

D is incorrect because ACE inhibitors have no impact on heart rate. Patients taking beta-blockers are taught to check their pulse before taking their medication and hold if the heart rate is below 60 bpm.

24. A patient has been given a first dose of captopril for heart failure, and the nurse is implementing interventions to prevent complications. Which is a priority intervention for this patient?

    A. Give the medication with food to prevent nausea and increase absorption
    B. Teach the patient to call for help with getting out of bed
    C. Ask the unlicensed assistive personnel to assist the patient with bathing
    D. Assess potassium levels and for symptoms of hypokalemia

Rationale:

Correct answer: B

Angiotensin-converting enzyme (ACE) inhibitors block the conversion from angiotensin I to angiotensin II in the lungs, causing decreased blood pressure. These medications also cause decreased aldosterone secretion and sodium and fluid loss. ACE inhibitors are indicated for heart failure and hypertension. The initial dose of an ACE inhibitor can cause severe hypotension, termed the "first-dose effect." The patient must be taught to call for help before getting out of bed to prevent postural hypotension and a fall. This risk is greatest after the first dose is taken.

A is incorrect because ACE inhibitors do not have to be taken with food. Food actually blocks the absorption of ACE inhibitors, so they should be taken one hour before or two hours after a meal.

C is incorrect because hygiene and collaboration with the unlicensed assistive personnel is not priority. Activities of daily living should be performed as independently as possible for this patient.

D is incorrect because hyperkalemia can occur with ACE inhibitors, not hypokalemia, especially in patients with renal insufficiency.

25. A patient is assessed by the nurse an hour after taking isosorbide mononitrate. The patient states they have a headache. Which intervention should the nurse perform?

    A. Start oxygen therapy
    B. Hold the next scheduled dose of isosorbide mononitrate
    C. Encourage the patient to drink water
    D. Administer acetaminophen

Rationale:

Correct answer: D

Isosorbide mononitrate is a vasodilator which relaxes smooth muscles in blood vessel walls, making it easier for blood to flow through. Headaches commonly occur with this medication due to the vasodilatory effects, especially during the beginning stage of therapy. Patients should be informed of this and instructed to take acetaminophen if headache occurs.

A is incorrect because the patient does not have hypoxia, and oxygen will not treat or prevent headaches.

B is incorrect because the medication must be taken as prescribed to prevent angina and should not be discontinued abruptly.

C is incorrect because the patient is not dehydrated, and drinking water will not treat or prevent headaches with this medication.

26. A patient is being taught about digoxin by the nurse. Which statement should be included in the patient's teaching?

    A. "Do not take aspirin or aspirin-containing products."
    B. "Limit the intake of foods that contain potassium in your diet."

C. "If your pulse rate is less than 80 bpm, do not take the medication."

D. "Do not take an antacid within an hour of taking the medication."

Rationale:

Correct answer: D

Digoxin is a cardiac glycoside prescribed for heart conditions including atrial fibrillation, flutter, and heart failure. Gastrointestinal absorption of digoxin can be erratic. Antacids interfere with absorption of digoxin. Adverse reactions to digoxin include anorexia, nausea, bradycardia, visual disturbances, and confusion.

A is incorrect because aspirin will have no impact on the absorption of digoxin.

B is incorrect because hypokalemia can potentiate digoxin toxicity. Patients taking this medication should be instructed to increase their intake of potassium-rich foods such as: bananas, potatoes with skin-on, sweet potatoes, white beans, avocado, dark leafy greens, dried apricots, and acorn squash. The nurse should monitor renal function and electrolytes.

C is incorrect because patients are taught to not take digoxin when bradycardic, but a heart rate of 80 bpm is within normal limits and not an indication to hold digoxin.

27. A nurse is teaching a patient about caring for themself at home after being diagnosed with heart failure. Which statement is most important for the nurse to include in the patient's discharge teaching?

    A. "Limit your fluids to less than three quarts per day."
    B. "Be sure to consume three balanced meals daily."
    C. "Take an additional diuretic when you feel short of breath."
    D. "Record your weight daily wearing the same amount of clothing."

Rationale:

Correct answer: D

Patients with heart failure must weigh daily to identify worsening heart failure and avoid complications early. Increasing dyspnea, intolerance of activity, symptoms of cold, and nocturia are also signs of worsening heart failure. The patient should eat a heart-healthy diet, balance intake of fluids with output, and take their medications as ordered. Daily weight and hypertension control are the most important points to teach patients with heart failure.

A is incorrect because intake of too much fluid can worsen symptoms of heart failure. Three quarts is over 2.8 L of fluid. A normal daily fluid intake is 2-2.5 L/day, so a heart failure patient may be on fluid restriction, such as 1.5 L/day.

B is incorrect because fluid balance is a greater priority than nutritional intake. Patients with heart failure often experience bloating and nausea due to abdominal ascites, so eating smaller frequent meals may be indicated.

C is incorrect because medications including diuretics should be taken as prescribed. Diuretics are not generally prescribed PRN. If the patient experiences symptoms such as shortness of breath, the healthcare provider should be notified.

28. A patient with type I diabetes is experiencing heart failure exacerbation. As the nurse admits the patient to the cardiac unit, what is the first action the nurse should take?

    A. Assess the respiratory status of the patient
    B. Assess the patient's serum electrolytes
    C. Administer intravenous furosemide
    D. Call the healthcare provider to obtain orders

Rationale:

Correct answer: A

Respiratory assessment and oxygenation status are the most important to assess for this patient. Heart failure exacerbation or decompensation is characterized by ejection fraction less than 40%, hypotension, pulmonary congestion, worsening fatigue, dyspnea with or without activity, and coughing with pink or blood-tinged sputum. The nurse's greatest priority is assessment of the current (baseline) airway status. The lungs will continue to be monitored closely as interventions are initiated. Respiratory and cardiac arrest are both complications that the nurse will be anticipating.

B is incorrect because electrolyte monitoring is important for heart failure patients but not priority over respiratory status.

C is incorrect because administration of diuretics is important for heart failure patients but not priority over respiratory status. The nurse must assess lung sounds before giving furosemide so the effect of the medication can be measured after the patient diuresis fluid.

D is incorrect because assessment of the current respiratory status is more important than obtaining orders for patient care. The nurse needs to remain focused on the patient at the bedside.

29. A patient with a history of mitral valve stenosis is on the cardiac unit. When assessing the patient, which clinical manifestation should the nurse recognize as progression of stenosis?

    A. Oxygen saturation level of 92%
    B. Fatigue and shortness of breath on exertion
    C. Systolic murmur
    D. Rheumatic fever

Rationale:

Correct answer: B

The mitral valve (also known as the bicuspid) is the atrio-ventricular valve in the left side of the heart. Shortness of breath or dyspnea on exertion manifests as the mitral valve orifice is narrowed (stenosed) and the pressure in the lungs increases. The heart has decreased ability and capacity to pump blood to the lungs and periphery, causing backup of blood in the lungs and fatigue due to the extra work of breathing. Medications to help treat symptoms of mitral valve stenosis include diuretics and blood-thinners (to prevent clots from forming).

A is incorrect because oxygen saturation levels are not directly related to mitral valve stenosis.

C is incorrect because a systolic murmur is not related to mitral valve stenosis.

D is incorrect because rheumatic fever is not a sign of worsening mitral valve stenosis. Rheumatic fever is a complication of untreated strep throat or scarlet fever and is the most common cause of mitral valve stenosis.

30. A patient is recovering after valve replacement surgery using a prosthetic valve. The patient asks why anticoagulants must be taken for the rest of their life. What is the best response by the nurse?

   A. "You are at greater risk of a heart attack with the prosthetic valve."
   B. "Artificial replacement valves form blood clots more than tissue valves."
   C. "You have reduced circulation in your leg where they took the vein."
   D. "There are small clots located in your heart and lungs due to the surgery."

Rationale:

Correct answer: B

Platelets can collect easily on synthetic valves and scar tissue, initiating formation of blood clots. Artificial valves are long-lasting as they are made of durable material, but there is an increased risk of clot formation necessitating the use of long-term anticoagulation medication. Thus, the patient is at higher risk for bleeding.

A is incorrect because there is not a greater risk of myocardial infarction with a prosthetic valve. Complications after a valve replacement include valve failure and prosthetic valvular endocarditis (PVE.)

C is incorrect because veins are not harvested from the leg for valve replacement surgery.

D is incorrect because valve replacement surgery does not generally cause thrombi or clots to form in the heart or lungs. The purpose of life-long anticoagulation therapy is to prevent clots.

31. A patient had mitral valve replacement surgery and has been prescribed warfarin. When the nurse performs discharge instructions, which patient statement demonstrates the need for more teaching?

   E. "I can carry heavy loads after six months."
   F. "I will go to the dentist in two weeks to have my teeth cleaned."
   G. "I shouldn't eat foods like spinach that are high in vitamin K."
   H. "I should use an electric razor instead of a straight blade."

Rationale:

Correct answer: B

Patients are placed on anticoagulant therapy, such as warfarin, to prevent blood clots from growing on a new valve. Patients should be instructed to avoid going to the dentist for six months after valve replacement surgery as there is an increased risk of bleeding, even from minor dental procedures.

A is incorrect because heavy lifting should be avoided for six months after valve surgery, indicating patient understanding.

C is incorrect because if warfarin is prescribed, the patient should avoid consuming foods with high levels of vitamin K, indicating patient understanding. (Vitamin K is the antidote to warfarin, and can lessen the anticoagulant effects of the medication, increasing risk for blood clots.)

D is incorrect because patients should be instructed to use an electric razor while on anticoagulant therapy, indicating patient understanding. Other bleeding precautions include using a soft-bristled toothbrush, avoiding contact sports or activities that have a high risk for falling. Bruising, falls, diarrhea, rash, severe or unusual headache, and fever should be reported to the healthcare provider.

32. In order to safely care for the patient with infective endocarditis, which infection control precautions should be used by the nurse?

    A. Standard precautions
    B. Bleeding precautions
    C. Reverse isolation
    D. Contact isolation

Rationale:

Correct answer: A

Infective endocarditis can be caused by several different organisms including streptococci, staphylococcus aureus, and fungi. This can be due to a skin abscess, infected gums, urinary tract infection, IV drug abuse, and even medical and surgical procedures. Infective endocarditis has no specific threat for transmission of causative organism. Standard precautions are sufficient for this patient.

B is incorrect because although thrombosis is an element of infective endocarditis, anticoagulation therapy is contraindicated. Bleeding precautions are required, and they are not a form of infection control precautions.

C is incorrect because the patient with infective endocarditis is not immunocompromised and does not need to be shielded from potential infection. Reverse isolation is necessary to prevent immunocompromised people from becoming infected by others or objects. This type of isolation may be used for those undergoing chemotherapy, awaiting bone marrow transplant, or on neutropenic precautions. Note: the CDC no longer recognizes reverse isolation as effective because of the negative psychosocial effects on patients.

D is incorrect because there is no specific threat for transmission of causative organism with infective endocarditis. Contact precautions are required for patients with infections from multi-drug resistant organisms (MRSA, VRE), C-diff, RSV, rotavirus, and Hep A.

33. The nurse is caring for a patient diagnosed with pericarditis. Which of the following assessment findings should be expected?

    A. Heart rate fluctuation between bradycardia and tachycardia
    B. Friction rub at the left lower sternal border
    C. Regular gallop rhythm
    D. Crackles in bilateral lung bases

Rationale:

Correct answer: B

Pericarditis is inflammation of the pericardium and can be characterized by pericardial friction rub and stabbing chest pain that typically worsens with deep inspiration and coughing. The pericardium is made up of three layers: an outer fibrous layer and two inner serous membrane layers. Pericarditis may cause pericardial friction rub at the left lower sternal border as a result of the inflamed inner pericardial layers rubbing together.

A is incorrect because heart rate changes are not specific to pericarditis.

C is incorrect because regular gallop rhythm is not specific to pericarditis. Complications the nurse will monitor for include heart palpitations and low-grade fever.

D is incorrect because crackles in lung bases are not specific to pericarditis. These symptoms are more indicative of left-sided heart failure or fluid volume overload.

34. The nurse cares for a patient who has received a heart transplant. The nurse teaches the patient that they should change positions slowly. When the patient asks why it is important, what is the best response by the nurse?

   A. "Quick position changes may cause shear and friction which can tear out internal vascular sutures."
   B. "The vascular connections are sensitive to changes in position, which can increase intravascular pressure and cause dizziness."
   C. "The new heart is not connected to your nervous system and cannot respond to changes in blood pressure from changes in position."
   D. "As your heart recovers, your blood flow is diverted away from your brain which increases your risk for stroke upon standing."

Rationale

Correct answer: C

The new transplanted heart is not connected to the nervous system, so baroreceptors and compensatory mechanisms do not function in response to position changes. This can lead to orthostatic hypotension, which can cause light-headedness and dizziness when changing positions quickly. This can be uncomfortable for the patient and increase risk for falls.

A is incorrect because it is an untrue statement.

B is incorrect because the vascular changes can cause decreased intravascular pressure, not increased.

D is incorrect because it is an untrue statement and does not specifically address the patient's question.

35. A patient who had heart transplant surgery is prescribed cyclosporine. Which statement should be included by the nurse in the patient's discharge teaching?

   A. "Don't floss and use a soft toothbrush."
   B. "Avoid crowds and sick people."
   C. "Position changes should be done slowly to avoid hypotension."
   D. "We will draw blood periodically to check for pancreas damage while you are taking this medication."

Rationale:

Correct answer: B

Medications such as cyclosporine suppress the immune system, which puts the patient at risk for infection. These medications are required to prevent the immune system from attacking the transplanted organ and causing organ failure. The patient should avoid crowds of people where diseases may easily be transmitted. Other precautions include not consuming undercooked foods, avoiding contact with soil and live plants, washing fruits and vegetables thoroughly (or buy canned / frozen instead), good handwashing, and flossing and brushing teeth between meals.

A is incorrect because these are instructions for a patient who has a bleeding risk. Cyclosporine does not increase risk for bleeding. Cyclosporine may cause thrush, so the patient should use nystatin swish-and-swallow QID.

C is incorrect because there is no risk for orthostatic hypotension. An adverse reaction to cyclosporine is hypertension.

D is incorrect because cyclosporine does not affect the pancreas. BUN, creatinine, and liver function tests are necessary when taking cyclosporine.

36. A female patient with end stage heart failure is on the list for transplant. The patient seems depressed and tells the nurse, "I know this is my last chance, but if the surgery goes wrong, I really don't want to end up with a tracheostomy for life." What is the best response by the nurse?

   A. "Would you like for me to call the chaplain?"
   B. "I will arrange for the psychiatrist to come speak to you."
   C. "We can remove you from the transplant list, if you choose."
   D. "Can I provide you with information about advance directives?"

Rationale:

Correct answer: D

The patient has verbalized fear or concern about outcomes of the surgery. Anxiety can have negative outcomes due to sympathetic stimulation. Allowing the patient to verbalize concerns and work on a positive outcome is the best action. The nurse can educate the patient about advance directives to help her plan her own care. A living will can indicate treatment or life-saving measures to be used if the patient is not able to make decisions for herself after surgery. A Durable Power of Attorney allows the patient to delegate another competent adult to make decisions for her, in the event that she becomes incompetent.

A is incorrect because the nurse should address this patient's concerns at the bedside. Calling the chaplain at this time is "passing the buck." The chaplain will be called to help address spiritual needs or concerns.

B is incorrect because the patient's concerns should not be pushed off on the psychiatrist.

C is incorrect because although the patient has a right to choose, taking the patient off the transplant list is jumping to a conclusion that the patient does not want the surgery.

37. The clinic nurse is assessing a 58-year-old woman who lives alone with her dog. Her diagnosis is heart failure. Which is the best question for the nurse to ask in order to assess heart failure severity in this patient?

   A. "Are you able to play with your dog without any shortness of breath?"
   B. "Tell me about your morning routine at home and what it feels like when you're getting ready each day."
   C. "Do you have any problems at night?"
   D. "Do you feel heaviness in your legs?"

Rationale:

Correct answer: B

This is an open statement that will give the nurse information about whether the patient is symptomatic while arising from bed, getting dressed, walking around the house, and preparing/eating breakfast. Heart failure patients usually have negative findings, including shortness of breath, dizziness, and fatigue while active. The patient's activity level needs to be assessed, and the nurse must determine if symptoms are present at rest, during mild exertion, or while fully active. This will indicate whether or not the heart failure has increased in severity.

A is incorrect because it is a closed-ended question and only gives the nurse one piece of information. The patient may be able to play with her dog while sitting in a chair, which does not require much physical activity. A better question to ask would be, "Are you able to take your dog for walks without complications?"

C is incorrect because nighttime breathlessness does not demonstrate the extent of heart failure. This is a yes/no question which does not give much information.

D is incorrect because peripheral edema is common in heart failure and does not determine extent.

38. An older patient with heart failure expresses concern about being dependent upon her daughter but is afraid to care for herself. She states she should probably die. What is the best response by the nurse?

    A. "Do you want to talk some more about your feelings?"
    B. "You're lucky to have a devoted daughter."
    C. "Your feelings of being a burden are normal."
    D. "Perhaps a visit from pastoral care will be helpful. What is your religious preference?"

Rationale:

Correct answer: A

Patients with heart failure, especially older patients, can experience depression. This can be due to decreasing ability to care for themselves or loss of independence. Encouraging the patient to talk about her feelings is therapeutic. The nurse can then inform her of available resources to assist her as needed. Use of open-ended communication provides for honest responses by the patient.

B is incorrect because it doesn't encourage the patient to talk about her concerns. This statement takes the focus off the patient.

C is incorrect because this answer is not as therapeutic as encouraging discussion in answer A.

D is incorrect because this statement does not enhance the nurse-client therapeutic relationship. The nurse should focus on the patient at the bedside and address concerns before calling pastoral care.

39. A patient with heart failure is being taught by the nurse about energy conservation. Which statement should the nurse include in this patient's teaching?

    A. "Walk until you feel short of breath, then head back home."

    B. "Before you begin chores, collect everything you need."

    C. "Instead of pushing or carrying, pull items that are more than five pounds."

    D. "Every day after dinner take a short walk to build strength."

Rationale:

Correct answer: B

Energy conservation is important for heart failure patients as even the lightest activity can cause fatigue. Collecting supplies before starting a chore decreases energy use and allows the patient to complete the chores without needing to move around the home for forgotten items.

A is incorrect because it puts the patient in danger. The patient should be instructed to walk short distances, gradually increasing the distance, so that no shortness of breath is experienced.

C is incorrect because pulling requires more energy than pushing or carrying.

D is incorrect because it does not decrease energy use.

40. A patient admitted with acute pericarditis calls the nurse to report substernal precordial pain radiating to the left side of his neck. Which non-pharmacologic comfort measure should the nurse implement?

    A. Place an ice pack on the patient's chest

    B. Provide neck rubs focusing on the left side

    C. Let the patient rest in bed with lights dimmed

    D. Have the patient sit up and lean forward on a pillow

Rationale:

Correct answer: D

Laying supine can worsen pain from acute pericarditis. The pain is described as a stabbing chest pain that worsens with coughing and deep breathing in addition to lying down. The usual comfortable position is upright and leaning forward. Gravity helps to take pressure off the pericardial muscle to decrease pain.

A is incorrect because ice packs will only have a superficial effect and will not likely relieve the inner pain located within the lining of the heart in this patient.

B is incorrect because neck rubs are more likely to increase pain in this patient.

C is incorrect because it does not provide pain relief.

NCLEX-RN – MED-SURG: RESPIRATORY – 40 QUESTIONS

1. A patient in the emergency department has esophageal trauma. Subcutaneous emphysema in the mediastinal area up to the lower part of the neck is palpated by the nurse. What is the priority action the nurse should take?

   A. A. Assess the patient's oxygenation status
   B. B. Obtain a STAT chest X-ray
   C. C. Prepare for immediate surgery
   D. D. Start two large-bore IVs

   Rationale:

   Correct answer: A

   Subcutaneous emphysema occurs when air or another gas such as CO2 gets into the tissues under the subcutaneous tissue. The nursing assessment reveals a crackling sensation under the skin during palpation. This is a potential complication of a ruptured esophagus. Airway is the priority in care because the patency of the patient's airway may be compromised. Thus, the priority in this option is to assess the patient's oxygenation status and observe for respiratory distress: tachypnea, dyspnea, shortness of breath, tachycardia, and abnormal or absent lung sounds.

   B is incorrect because immediate airway assessment at the bedside is the priority over diagnostic procedures.

   C is incorrect because the airway must be assessed and maintained before a surgical procedure.

D is incorrect because IV access is important and will help the nurse infuse fluids and medications, but the airway is initially more important than circulatory volume or IV medications.

2. A patient with hepatopulmonary syndrome is experiencing dyspnea, and his oxygen saturation level is 92%. He says he doesn't want to wear oxygen because it causes nosebleeds. He insists the nurse leave his room and leave him alone. Which action should the nurse take?

    A. Instruct the patient to sit as upright as possible
    B. Add humidity to the oxygen and encourage the patient to wear it
    C. Document the patient's refusal and notify the healthcare provider
    D. Contact the healthcare provider to request an additional dose of the patient's diuretic

Rationale:

Correct answer: A

Hepatopulmonary syndrome is an uncommon condition that affects the lungs of people with advanced liver disease. Symptoms include hypoxemia as a result of dilation of blood vessels. This makes it hard for the lungs to deliver adequate amounts of oxygen to the body, causing dyspnea. This patient's oxygenation status is low, so sitting upright should be the first intervention.

B is incorrect because the first intervention should be sitting the patient upright. The higher the head of the bed, the easier it is to breathe. Then the nurse can add humidity to the oxygen.

C is incorrect because documentation and notification of the healthcare provider should occur, but this is not priority. The nurse must immediately address the dyspnea and low oxygen saturation.

D is incorrect because an additional dose of diuretic could risk hypovolemia and electrolyte imbalance. This will not correct the condition. Hepatopulmonary syndrome is ultimately only correctable with a liver transplant.

3. A nurse is preparing a patient for paracentesis. Which intervention is appropriate for the nurse delegate to an unlicensed assistive personnel (UAP)?

33

A. Have the patient sign the informed consent

B. Assist the patient to void before the procedure

C. Help the patient lay flat in bed on the right side

D. Get the patient into a chair after the procedure

Rationale:

Correct answer: B

Paracentesis is accessing a body cavity with a needle to remove a fluid collection or gas where it does not belong. The procedure is done to remove fluid from around the lungs or the abdominal cavity to improve breathing ability and oxygenation status. Voiding should occur just before a paracentesis procedure to prevent bladder puncture. Other appropriate nursing actions include checking baseline weight and vital signs before the paracentesis, monitoring BP during the procedure, and assessing dressing for drainage after the procedure.

A is incorrect because the healthcare provider is responsible for obtaining the signed informed consent. The nurse may act as the witness.

C is incorrect because the correct position for paracentesis is sitting upright in bed or on the side of the bed leaning over bedside table.

D is incorrect because the patient should be on bed rest after paracentesis.

4. A patient is in the emergency room after being stung by a bee. The patient is experiencing anxiety and difficulty breathing. What priority action should the nurse perform?

A. Have the patient lie down

B. Assess the patient's airway

C. Administer high-flow oxygen

D. Remove the stinger from the site

Rationale:

Correct answer: B

With any patient experiencing difficulty breathing, the initial action is to assess and maintain airway.

A is incorrect because lying down would not help the patient's breathing. The correct position for a patient with breathing difficulties is head of bed elevated.

34

C is incorrect because the nurse should elevate the head of bed and then start low-flow oxygen and reassess for improvement.

D is incorrect because removing the stinger may be appropriate, but it is not priority. After oxygenation has been addressed, the nurse can then proceed to remove the stinger with a flat edge such as a credit card. (Tweezers should not be used, because they can release additional venom into the patient as the stinger is squeezed for removal.)

5. A patient admitted for Pneumocystis jiroveci pneumonia reports activity-related shortness of breath and extreme fatigue. The nurse will promote comfort with which of the following interventions?

    A. Administer sleeping medication
    B. Perform most activities for the patient
    C. Increase the patient's oxygen during activity
    D. Pace activities, allowing for adequate rest

Rationale:

Correct answer: D

In patients with pneumonia, decreased oxygenation status and infection cause fatigue and shortness of breath. The nurse should encourage patients to participate in as much of their care as they possibly can, keeping them independent. The nurse should pace activities, allowing for adequate rest in between.

A is incorrect because sleeping medication may be indicated, but not as a first step. The nurse should try non-pharmacologic measures to promote rest before adding a sleep aid.

B is incorrect because the patient should be allowed to do as much as they can for themselves, promoting independence.

C is incorrect because increased oxygen is only required if the patient's saturation drops while active.

6. The nursing instructor is supervising several nursing students on the medical surgical floor. When a student asks why chronic obstructive pulmonary disease leads to polycythemia, what is the best response by the nursing instructor?

A. It is due to side effects of medications for bronchodilation

B. It is from overactive bone marrow in response to chronic disease

C. It combats the anemia caused by an increased metabolic rate

D. It compensates for tissue hypoxia caused by lung disease

Rationale:

Correct answer: D

Polycythemia is increase in red blood cell numbers in response to the lung disease. Red blood cells are produced in a response to hypoxia, which leads to more oxygen carrying capacity and ability to deliver oxygen to tissues.

A is incorrect because polycythemia is not a side effect of a bronchodilator medications. Note: anabolic steroids used by athletes can cause polycythemia.

B is incorrect because polycythemia can be an effect of overactive bone marrow, but patients with COPD do not often have overactive bone marrow.

C is incorrect because polycythemia is not a response to anemia.

7. While in triage in a busy emergency room, the nurse assesses a patient who has symptoms of tuberculosis. Which is the first action the nurse should take?

A. Place a mask on the patient and the nurse

B. Administer intravenous 0.9% saline solution

C. Transfer the patient to a negative pressure room

D. Obtain a sputum culture and sensitivity

Rationale:

Correct answer: A

Tuberculosis is a highly contagious respiratory infection that is spread through airborne means. When TB is suspected, the nurse must first place a mask on their own face and then the patient's.

B is incorrect because the greatest priority is prevention of the spread of this highly contagious disease, not fluid infusion.

C is incorrect because the patient must be wearing a mask before they are transferred within the hospital. Patients who exhibit signs and symptoms of tuberculosis must be placed in a negative pressure room in order to prevent staff, patients, and family members from possibly being infected. However, the transfer cannot occur until the nurse ensures the safety of those who may come into contact with the patient during the transfer.

D is incorrect because while a sputum culture and sensitivity are indicated, they are not the first action.

8. A person in the public park is stung by a bee and encountered by a nurse. The person's lips are swollen and wheezes are easily heard. What is the first action the nurse should take?

    A. Elevate the site and notify the person's next of kin

    B. Remove the stinger with tweezers and encourage rest

    C. Administer topical diphenhydramine, apply ice, and call 911

    D. Administer an EpiPen from the first aid kit

Rationale:

Correct answer: D

Swollen lips indicate anaphylaxis, and this is a true medical emergency. The EpiPen should be administered at the first sign of anaphylaxis, if available. Then the patient should be transported to the closest emergency room, and the nurse should frequently assess the airway while in transport.

A is incorrect because elevating this site is not a treatment for airway obstruction from anaphylaxis.

B is incorrect because removing the stinger will not treat airway obstruction from anaphylaxis. Tweezers are not the best method for removing the stinger because they can release additional venom into the patient as the stinger is squeezed for removal. The stinger should be removed with a flat edge such as a credit card.

C is incorrect because topical diphenhydramine will not treat airway obstruction from anaphylaxis. Ice will reduce swelling at the site of the sting but not treat the airway. Calling 911 is not an inappropriate nursing action, but the EpiPen should be administered first.

9. A patient arrives in the emergency room with full-thickness burns to the lower extremities from a structure fire. The patient is occasionally disoriented, has a headache, and has 0.9 normal saline running at 100 ml/hr through a peripheral IV. Which of the following actions should be taken by the nurse?

    A. Increase the patient's oxygen and obtain arterial blood gases
    B. Draw a blood sample for a carboxyhemoglobin level
    C. Change the fluid to Lactated Ringers and increase the infusion rate
    D. Perform a thorough Mini-Mental State Examination

Rationale:

Correct answer: C

The emergent phase following a burn is the first 24-48 hours. The patient is likely to exhibit hypotension from fluid loss (from open wounds or extravasation into deeper tissues.) LR or plasma is infused rapidly over the first eight hours, and more slowly over the next 16 hours.

A is incorrect because fluids are priority. The disorientation and headache are signs of carbon monoxide poisoning, which will not be revealed with an ABG.

B is incorrect because fluids are priority. Being in a fire in an enclosed space increases risk for carbon monoxide poisoning. Carboxyhemoglobin blood levels should be drawn after fluids have been addressed.

D is incorrect because a Mini-Mental State Examination will not address the fluids needs or give information related to carbon monoxide poisoning.

10. A patient rescued from a house fire has burns on the arms, legs, and chest. Eight hours after admission, the patient has become restless and agitated. What is the first action the nurse should take?

    A. Remain at the bedside and comfort the patient
    B. Administer morphine IV
    C. Assess the patient's orientation and level of consciousness
    D. Check pulse oximetry for oxygenation status

Rationale:

Correct answer: D

The patient may have experienced smoke inhalation injury. Agitation is an indication of hypoxia. Pulse oximetry is the priority assessment as it gives here-and-now information about the patient's current respiratory status.

A is incorrect because comforting the patient will not help with agitation in the hypoxemic patient. The nurse must treat physical problems first.

B is incorrect because morphine will treat pain but does not address potential hypoxia.

C is incorrect because the nurse does not need further LOC assessment at this time. Airway assessment is priority.

11. A patient rescued from a house fire has sustained burns to the face and upper chest. As the patient arrives by ambulance, the nurse notes the patient has a bolus of LR infusing and 4L/min O2 by face mask applied. Which of the following actions should be taken by the nurse first?

    A. Auscultate lung sounds
    B. Determine depth and extent of burns
    C. Infuse TPN with high-protein concentration
    D. Administer hydromorphone

Rationale:

Correct answer: A

The patient with burns to the head, neck, upper back, chest or upper extremities is at high risk for inhalation injury or burns to the structures of the airway. The nurse should not assume that a thorough airway assessment has been made or that the oxygen face mask is effective for meeting oxygen needs. Assessment of the airway and breathing is the first action the nurse should take.

B is incorrect because determining the depth and extent of burns is an important nursing assessment after airway has been addressed.

C is incorrect because protein is needed for wound healing, but LR is infused for the first 24-48 hours. Nutritional needs do not take priority over airway assessment, initially. Note: a high-calorie, high-carbohydrate, high-protein diet is needed for optimal healing of burns. Tube feeding or TPN may be indicated if the patient is not able to take in enough nutrition PO.

D is incorrect because administration of analgesics is important due to the extreme severe pain experienced by burn patients, but airway is priority.

12. A patient with lung cancer informs the nurse he has a 50-pack/year smoking history. Which of the following nursing actions is best?

    A. Encourage the patient to quit smoking to stop further cancer development

    B. Encourage the patient to be completely honest about both tobacco and marijuana use

    C. Maintain a nonjudgmental attitude to avoid causing the patient to feel guilty

    D. Educate the patient about cancer treatment options and prognosis

Rationale:

Correct answer: C

Cigarettes, cigars, pipe tobacco, and marijuana are all part of smoking history. The patient may have guilt or denial related to this, so a nonjudgmental attitude should be assumed by the nurse during the interview to encourage the patient to be honest.

A is incorrect because quitting may not stop the cancer from spreading.

B is incorrect because this may suggest distrust and is non-therapeutic.

D is incorrect because the nurse is not responsible for initially educating the patient about his treatment options. That is the role of the healthcare provider. The nurse must remain focused on the nurse-patient relationship and maintain a nonjudgmental attitude.

13. The nurse is caring for a patient recovering after an open lung biopsy procedure. Which expected nursing assessment is matched with the correct nursing intervention?

    A. Patient has leaking fluid from needle site, so nurse applies a new, sterile dressing

    B. Patient's heart rate is 55 beats/min, so nurse withholds pain medication

    C. Patient has reduced breath sounds, so nurse calls physician immediately

    D. Patient's respiratory rate is 18 breaths/min, so nurse decreases oxygen flow rate

Rationale:

Correct answer: C

Lung biopsy can be performed using an open (surgical) or closed (through skin or trachea) procedure. Samples of lung tissue are removed to determine if cancer or lung disease is present. The risk for pneumothorax (lung collapse) is greater with an open procedure. Pneumothorax is a serious complication which requires chest tube insertion for lung re-expansion. If the nurse notes decreased breath sounds (a sign of pneumothorax), the healthcare provider must be notified immediately. Other signs of pneumothorax include shortness of breath, tachycardia, and bluish discoloration of skin (late sign).

A is incorrect because a needle is not used during an open biopsy procedure. If any leaking is noted from the needle insertion site after a closed biopsy procedure, the nurse should reinforce the sterile dressing and call the healthcare provider.

B is incorrect because bradycardia is not an indication for withholding pain medication.

D is incorrect because a respiratory rate of 18 is normal and does not necessitate a decreased oxygen flow rate.

14. The nurse is assessing the health history of a patient. Which of the following data is highest priority for the nurse to collect when determining risks for respiratory disease?

   A. Daily fluid intake
   B. Neck circumference
   C. Height and weight
   D. Occupation and hobbies

Rationale:

Correct answer: D

Occupation and hobbies can be a source of chronic exposure to inhaled irritants and respiratory problems. Occupations at high risk for respiratory disease include welding, mining, furnace repair/installation, and work in plants with poor ventilation (chemical, plastic, or rubber plants).

A is incorrect because fluid intake is not directly linked to risk to respiratory disease.

B is incorrect because neck circumference is not important for assessment of respiratory risks. Neck circumference is used to determine obesity, complications with endotracheal tube placement, and sleep apnea, which is not a disease process.

C is incorrect because height and weight are important but aren't directly linked to respiratory disease.

15. The nurse is caring for a 68-year-old patient admitted for pulmonary infection. Which of the following actions should be taken by the nurse first?

    A. Encourage fluid intake
    B. Assess level of consciousness
    C. Raise head of bed to 60 degrees
    D. Provide humidified oxygen

Rationale:

Correct answer: B

Assessing level of consciousness is important in a patient with pulmonary infection because this helps the nurse determine if oxygen should be applied. Pulmonary infection affects oxygenation status and gas exchange which can limit cerebral oxygenation, leading to disorientation and drowsiness.

A is incorrect because fluid intake is important but not the first action.

C is incorrect because raising the head of the bed will facilitate breathing, but the nurse should gather assessment data before implementing.

D is incorrect because humidified oxygen will not be applied until the nurse has assessed the respiratory system. Not all patients with pulmonary infection necessarily need humidified oxygen.

16. The nurse has just auscultated the patient's breath sounds. Which finding is matched correctly with the nurse's intervention?

    A. Hollow sounds heard over the trachea, so the nurse increases the oxygen flow rate
    B. Crackles are heard in bases, so the nurse administers beclomethasone inhaler
    C. Wheezes are heard in central areas, so the nurse administers bronchodilator inhaler
    D. Vesicular sounds are heard over the periphery, so the nurse has the patient breathe deeply

Rationale:

Correct answer: C

Wheezes in the lungs indicate narrowed airways, which can be treated with bronchodilators to open airways.

A is incorrect because hollow sounds are normal in the trachea and no intervention is necessary.

B is incorrect because crackles in lung bases are an indication of fluid in the interstitial spaces of the lungs. The patient should be encouraged to cough. Crackles that don't clear with coughing may indicate pulmonary edema. Beclomethasone is a corticosteroid (generally used twice a day) to prevent asthma symptoms such as chest tightness, difficulty breathing, coughing, and wheezing. This is not a rescue inhaler and will not help clear crackles.

D is incorrect because vesicular sounds in the periphery are normal and no intervention is necessary.

17. A 55-year-old male patient has measurements of the anteroposterior (AP) and lateral chest diameter that are equal. Which question should be asked by the nurse?

    A. "Do you take any medications or herbal supplements?"
    B. "Do you have chronic breathing problems?"
    C. "How often do you exercise?"
    D. "Have you been exposed to any allergens lately?"

Rationale:

Correct answer: B

In a normal chest, the lateral diameter should be two times the AP diameter (1:1 until the age of six). This patient has a 1:1 AP to Lateral diameter, known as a 'barrel chest,' which can be a result of long-term chronic breathing problems such as chronic obstructive pulmonary disease or asthma.

A is incorrect because medications and herbal supplements are not associated with barrel chest.

C is incorrect because exercise is not associated with barrel chest.

D is incorrect because allergies do not cause barrel chest. The nurse should assess for the presence of chronic respiratory issues as well as occupation and hobbies that may expose the patient to irritants that lead to chronic respiratory problems.

18. A patient is scheduled for a thoracentesis this morning. Before the procedure, which intervention should be completed by the nurse?

    A. Measure oxygen saturation before and after a 12-minute walk
    B. Verify that the patient understands all possible complications
    C. Explain the procedure in detail to the patient and the family
    D. Validate that informed consent has been signed by the patient

Rationale:

Correct answer: D

Thoracentesis is a procedure in which a needle is inserted into the pleural space between the lungs and the chest wall. This procedure is performed to remove excess fluid (pleural effusion) from the pleural space to facilitate easier breathing or send for biopsy. Informed consent is required before any invasive procedure. Complications may include pneumothorax, bleeding, bruising, infection, and, in rare cases, liver or spleen injuries.

A is incorrect because oxygen saturation before and after a 12-minute walk is not required before a thoracentesis.

B is incorrect because understanding of complications is verified by the healthcare provider.

C is incorrect because explanation of the procedure is performed by the healthcare provider.

19. The nurse cares for a patient following a thoracentesis procedure. The dressing is on the left side of the posterior thorax. Which finding requires immediate action?

    A. The patient rates pain as a 5/10 at the site of the procedure
    B. Serosanguinous drainage on dressing
    C. Pulse oximetry is 93% on 2 liters of oxygen
    D. The trachea is deviated toward the right side of the neck

Rationale:

Correct answer: D

Tracheal deviation is a sign of tension pneumothorax—a medical emergency. Tension pneumothorax is collection of air or fluid in the pleural cavity that causes the affected lung to shift in the opposite direction, which also shifts the trachea.

A is incorrect because pain is expected after thoracentesis and does not require immediate action.

B is incorrect because although this is not an expected finding, tracheal deviation is the greatest concern.

C is incorrect because although this is a low pulse-ox reading, this may be expected after a thoracentesis depending on whether lung disease is present. This should be investigated by the nurse, but tracheal deviation is the priority.

20. The nurse is caring for a patient recovering from bronchoscopy two hours ago. When the patient asks for ice cream to soothe their sore throat, what is the next action the nurse should take?

    A. Notify the healthcare provider and request a diet order
    B. Give the patient ice chips
    C. Assess gag reflex before giving water
    D. Give the patient a sip to assess swallowing ability

Rationale:

Correct answer: C

During a bronchoscopy, a flexible tube is inserted into the trachea. This procedure can be used for visualization of the lower airways, removal of a foreign object from the trachea/lungs, or sputum/tissue sample collection. A topical anesthetic is sprayed in the patient's throat, and the patient may be sedated for the procedure, which affects the patient's ability to swallow. The gag reflex should be checked before giving the patient anything by mouth.

A is incorrect because notifying the healthcare provider is not necessary. Standard procedure following a bronchoscopy is to keep the patient NPO until drowsiness subsides. When alert

45

and oriented, the nurse must assess for a positive gag reflex before allowing the patient to take anything by mouth. Then clear liquids are acceptable, progressing to a regular diet.

B is incorrect because the patient may aspirate if the gag reflex has not returned.

D is incorrect because the gag reflex should be assessed first, and then the nurse can offer a sip of water to assess swallowing ability.

21. A patient experiences dyspnea and has to stop several times when climbing stairs. When planning care for this patient, which intervention should be included by the nurse?

    A. Assistance with activities of daily living
    B. Physical therapy activities every day
    C. Oxygen therapy at 2 liters per nasal cannula
    D. Complete bedrest with frequent repositioning

Rationale:

Correct answer: A

This patient has class III dyspnea, which is characterized by dyspnea upon completing activities. Assistance should be provided with activities, but the patient should be encouraged to remain as independent as possible.

B is incorrect because help with ADLs addresses the safety issue. Safety is priority over physical therapy daily.

C is incorrect because oxygen is only necessary if the patient is hypoxic.

D is incorrect because the patient does not require complete bedrest. The nurse should encourage the patient to stay active and address safety needs.

22. A patient was administered benzocaine spray by the nurse before bronchoscopy earlier today. The patient now has low oxygen saturation levels and cyanosis, despite oxygen administration via non-rebreather. What is the next action the nurse should take?

    A. Administer an albuterol treatment
    B. Notify the rapid response team
    C. Assess the patient's peripheral pulses
    D. Increase the oxygen flow rate

Rationale:

Correct answer: B

This patient has manifestations of methemoglobinemia, an adverse effect of the benzocaine spray. Increased levels of methemoglobin in the blood prevent hemoglobin from releasing oxygen throughout the body. This is a medical emergency and can lead to shock, seizures, and death. Symptoms include bluish coloring of the skin, headache, fatigue, shortness of breath, and lack of energy. Methemoglobinemia can also be caused by other medications such as are dapsone (an antibiotic used to treat leprosy), chloroquine (used to treat malaria), and nitrites (used to preserve meat.)

A is incorrect because albuterol is a bronchodilator and will not reverse the effects of the benzocaine spray. Bronchodilator inhalers are used to open airways when wheezing is present.

C is incorrect because assessment of pulses does not provide information related to the problem. The nurse does not need any more assessment at this time.

D is incorrect because the condition this patient is experiencing cannot be corrected with increased oxygen. Treatment includes methylene blue, ascorbic acid, hyperbaric oxygen therapy, or red blood cell transfusion.

23. A nurse admits a new patient to the medical surgical unit. While assessing lung sounds, the nurse places the stethoscope over the trachea and larynx and hears a harsh, hollow sound. What is the first action the nurse should take?

    A. Document the findings
    B. Administer oxygen therapy
    C. Position the patient in high-Fowler's position
    D. Administer albuterol

Rationale:

Correct answer: A

Harsh, hollow sounds over the trachea and larynx are bronchial breath sounds and are a normal finding. This should be documented in the patient's chart. Documentation is appropriate when no other intervention is necessary and when no other direct patient care options are available as answer choices.

B is incorrect because oxygen therapy is not indicated.

C is incorrect because position changes are not indicated.

D is incorrect because albuterol is not indicated with normal breath sounds.

24. A patient is on 2 liters per minute of oxygen via nasal cannula. The nursing student removes the oxygen according to the healthcare provider's order. The patient says, "I need that still, or I won't be getting any oxygen." What is the correct response by the student nurse?

    A. "If you desaturate or show signs of hypoxia, we will reapply the nasal cannula."
    B. "The room air is actually 21% oxygen. We will monitor you closely and make sure you are able to breathe without difficulty."
    C. "I think you will be ok without it."
    D. "The doctor ordered for the oxygen to be removed."

Rationale:

Correct answer: B

This answer choice provides information, responds to the patient's concern, and offers reassurance. After removing oxygen, the student nurse (and the nurse) will monitor for pulse-ox desaturation, shortness of breath, disorientation, and other signs of hypoxia. Oxygen will be reapplied if these assessments are made.

A is incorrect because the student nurse should not assume that the patient will understand medical terms such as "desaturate" or "hypoxia." The student nurse must communicate in a way that the patient will understand.

C is incorrect because it dismisses the patient's concern, and it focuses on the student nurse.

D is incorrect because it does not focus on the patient's concern or provide enough information to reassure the patient.

25. The nurse prepares a patient for a tracheostomy procedure scheduled in one hour. What is the priority action by the nurse?

A. Administer anxiolytic medication

B. Obtain verbal consent for the procedure

C. Reinforce pre-op teaching

D. Start preoperative antibiotic infusion

Rationale:

Correct answer: C

Tracheostomy is an invasive surgical procedure in which a new opening is created into the trachea for an artificial airway to be inserted. After the healthcare provider explains the procedure and obtains signed consent, the nurse is responsible for reinforcing teaching about the procedure and what to expect afterwards.

A is incorrect because anxiolytics are indicated, but the patient should be NPO. IV anxiolytics will be administered but not a full hour before the procedure. (IV meds will have effect more quickly; PO anxiolytics may take an hour to reach full effect.)

B is incorrect because written consent is obtained by the healthcare provider for a tracheostomy. The nurse signs as a witness but cannot obtain the consent.

D is incorrect because antibiotics are not often given prophylactically before tracheostomy placement.

26. A patient underwent surgical tracheostomy placement three days ago. While assessing the patient, the nurse discovers the face and eyelids are puffy and swollen. What is the priority action by the nurse?

    A. Assess the patient's oxygen saturation

    B. Notify the rapid response team

    C. Oxygenate the patient with a bag-valve-mask

    D. Palpate the skin of the upper chest

Rationale:

Correct answer: A

This patient has signs and symptoms of subcutaneous emphysema, air that leaks into tissues around the tracheostomy. Oxygenation status should be assessed by the nurse as priority.

B is incorrect because the rapid response team is notified if the patient is unstable. The nurse must first assess for hypoxia before determining whether the rapid response team needs to be called.

C is incorrect because oxygenation with a bag-valve-mask may not be indicated.

D is incorrect because the skin of the upper chest may be palpated to further assess the extent of the subcutaneous emphysema but not as priority.

27. The nurse discovers food particles when suctioning a patient's tracheostomy tube. What is the best action by the nurse?

    A. Elevate head of the patient's bed
    B. Measure and compare cuff pressures
    C. Place the patient on NPO status
    D. Request a swallow study

Rationale:

Correct answer: B

The patient may be suffering from tracheomalacia, a softening of the tracheal tissue and supporting tracheal cartilage. This can be a result of tissue necrosis caused by abnormally high tracheostomy cuff pressure. Tracheomalacia is often manifested by food in secretions. The nurse may also notice that greater pressure is needed to inflate the tracheostomy cuff than usual. The nurse should measure the current cuff pressure and compare it to previous pressures documented to determine if cuff pressure is high and how long it has been high. Normal cuff pressure is less than 25cm H20 (14-20 mmHg) and should generally be checked every eight hours.

A is incorrect because elevating the head of bed will not alleviate the situation or help determine the cause.

C is incorrect because NPO status will not alleviate the situation or help determine the cause.

D is incorrect because a swallow study will not alleviate or confirm tracheomalacia. A chest X-ray is the diagnostic tool needed to verify tracheomalacia.

28. A patient who had a tracheostomy placed four days ago is fed lunch by an unlicensed assistive personnel (UAP). That evening, the UAP tells the nurse the patient coughed frequently during lunch. What is the priority action by the nurse?

    A. Immediately assess the patient's lung sounds
    B. Assign a different patient to the UAP
    C. Report the UAP to the nursing supervisor
    D. Request thicker liquids for meals

Rationale:

Correct answer: A

Assessment of lung sounds and oxygenation is priority because this patient may have possibly aspirated.

B is incorrect because assigning the UAP a different patient does not address the safety of the initial tracheostomy patient. The nurse must provide adequate teaching to the UAP before any further patient care activities are performed on any patients.

C is incorrect because reporting the UAP to the supervisor should be done after the nurse assesses the patient and then reminds the UAP that abnormal findings (such as frequent coughing while feeding a patient) should always be reported to the RN immediately.

D is incorrect because thickening liquids is not priority and does not give any further information about the current status of the lungs.

29. Tracheostomy care for a patient is provided by the student nurse. During the procedure, which student action would require the instructor to intervene?

    A. Holding the device securely when changing ties
    B. Suctioning the patient prior to tracheostomy care
    C. Tying a square knot at the back of the neck
    D. Using half-strength hydrogen peroxide for cleansing

Rationale:

Correct answer: C

For patient safety, the knot should be placed at the side of the neck for easy access. This can also prevent pressure ulcers from forming at the back of the neck when the patient is laying supine.

A is incorrect because holding the device when changing ties is appropriate. This prevents the tracheostomy from becoming displaced, so no intervention is required.

B is incorrect because suctioning the patient for secretions is appropriate, so no intervention is required.

D is incorrect because half-strength hydrogen peroxide is appropriate for cleaning during trach care and rinsing the inner cannula. No intervention is necessary.

30. Tracheostomy skills are being practiced by a nursing student in the simulation lab. Which of the following student actions is an indication that additional teaching is necessary?

   A. Applying suction while inserting the catheter
   B. Preoxygenating the client prior to suctioning
   C. Suctioning for a total of three times, if needed
   D. Suctioning for only 10 to 15 seconds each time

Rationale:

Correct answer: A

When suctioning a patient, suction is only applied during withdrawal of the suction catheter. The nursing student should apply suction intermittently and slowly rotate the catheter between the dominant thumb and forefinger as the catheter is withdrawn. This will prevent causing hypoxia.

B is incorrect because preoxygenation is appropriate prior to suctioning. During the suctioning process, the patient will not be able to breathe as effectively through the tracheostomy tube, so it is important to hyperoxygenate before beginning the process. Thus, no additional teaching is necessary.

C is incorrect because suctioning should be limited to three times total. The patient should be hyperoxygenated between suction passes. No additional teaching is necessary.

D is incorrect because suctioning for 10-15 seconds is appropriate.

31. A patient is placed on oxygen via nasal cannula in the hospital. When the nurse assesses the patient, which finding indicates the patient is meeting goals for a priority diagnosis?

    A. 100% of meals being eaten by the patient

    B. Intact skin behind the ears

    C. The patient understanding the need for oxygen

    D. Unchanged weight for the past three days

Rationale:

Correct answer: B

Anything that applies pressure to the skin, such as oxygen tubing, can cause pressure ulcers. If the skin behind the patient' ears is intact, this indicates a goal for the nursing diagnosis "risk for impaired skin integrity" is met.

A is incorrect because although this is a good outcome, nutrition is not related to oxygenation.

C is incorrect because understanding the need for oxygen is important, but patient education is psychosocial. Physical needs are a greater priority.

D is incorrect because weight consistence is not related to oxygenation.

32. While assessing a patient, the nurse notes pulsation of the tracheostomy tube corresponding with the pulse rate. The nurse finds no other abnormal assessments. What is the most appropriate action by the nurse?

    A. Call the operating room to inform them of a pending emergency case

    B. No action is needed at this time; this is a normal finding

    C. Remove the tracheostomy tube and ventilate the patient with a bag-valve-mask

    D. Stay with the patient and have someone else call the provider immediately

Rationale:

Correct answer: D

A trachea-innominate artery fistula may have formed, which is life-threatening. This is an abnormal connection between the patient's trachea and a nearby artery. Through this connection, blood from within the artery may pass into the trachea or alternatively, air from within the trachea may cross into the artery. This is a complication from prolonged endotracheal intubation, cuff over-inflation, or poorly-placed endotracheal tube. Primary threats are respiratory compromise or hemorrhage. The nurse should stay with the patient (provide respiratory support, assess for hemorrhage). The nurse can delegate another member of the nursing team to call the healthcare provider immediately.

A is incorrect because the patient will need surgery, but the nurse does not schedule the OR. Bedside care of the deteriorating patient is priority.

B is incorrect because this is not a normal finding.

C is incorrect because the tube should only be removed if the patient starts hemorrhaging.

33. The nurse in the oncology clinic cares for a patient diagnosed with throat cancer. The patient had a tracheostomy placed one week ago. Which assessment finding indicates that goals for the nursing diagnosis related to self-esteem are being met?

    A. The patient demonstrates good understanding of stoma care
    B. The patient has joined a book club that meets weekly at the library
    C. Family members take turns assisting with stoma care
    D. Skin around the stoma is intact without signs of infection

Rationale:

Correct answer: B

An activity that requires the patient to be active in public with other individuals is the best sign for goals related to impaired self-esteem.

A is incorrect because stoma care is important for infection prevention and skin integrity but is not a direct indication of self-esteem.

C is incorrect because family members assisting with stoma care are unrelated to the nursing diagnosis.

D is incorrect because intact stoma skin is a good outcome, but is unrelated to the nursing diagnosis.

34. A patient is receiving oxygen via nasal cannula. What task may be performed by the unlicensed assistive personnel (UAP)?

A. Applying water-soluble ointment to nares and lips

B. Increasing the oxygen flow rate if the patient starts to decompensate

C. Removing the tubing from the patient's nose

D. Checking for reddened areas behind the ears where the cannula rests

Rationale:

Correct answer: A

Water-soluble ointment helps with preventing the drying that occurs with oxygen administration. This task is within the scope of practice for the UAP.

B is incorrect because the UAP is not able to make a judgment about whether or not the patient is deteriorating. The UAP can count breaths per minute and can read the pulse-oximetry, but abnormal findings must be reported to the nurse immediately. The nurse will then make the nursing judgment to increase the oxygen flow rate. The UAP cannot adjust oxygen flow.

C is incorrect because it is not within the UAP's scope of practice to remove oxygen.

D is incorrect because skin assessment is the responsibility of the RN, and this cannot be delegated.

35. Lunch has been delivered to a patient receiving oxygen via Venturi mask. What is the best action by the nurse?

    A. Assess the patient's oxygen saturation and, if normal, turn off the oxygen

    B. Determine if the patient can switch to a nasal cannula during the meal

    C. Have the patient replace the mask back on the face between bites of food

    D. Turn the oxygen off while the patient eats the meal and then restart it

Rationale:

Correct answer: B

Oxygen should be delivered constantly, and the nurse should check the patient's chart to see if switching this patient to a nasal cannula during meals has been approved. Otherwise, the nurse should contact the healthcare provider to discuss the issue.

A is incorrect because the oxygen should not be turned off.

C is incorrect because removing the oxygen supply to take bites will not meet the patient's oxygen needs.

D is incorrect because the oxygen should not be turned off.

36. A patient is receiving 50% oxygen via Venturi mask. The nurse assesses the oxygen adjunct and notes the mask fits appropriately and oxygen is flowing at 3 L/min. What is the best action by the nurse?

    A. Assess the patient's oxygen saturation
    B. Document these findings in the chart
    C. Immediately increase the flow rate
    D. Turn the flow rate down to 2 L/min

Rationale:

Correct answer: C

A Venturi mask is used to deliver a high flow of oxygen between 4 and 12 L/min. This type of oxygen delivery is used most often for critically ill patients who require a specific amount of oxygen administered. This patient's flow rate is low and should be increased by the nurse.

A is incorrect because oxygen saturation is assessed after flow rate adjusted.

B is incorrect because the flow rate is too low.

D is incorrect because the flow rate is too low.

37. A patient is admitted to the emergency room with a nasal fracture. What is the first assessment the nurse should perform?

    A. Facial pain
    B. Vital signs
    C. Bone displacement
    D. Airway patency

Rationale:

Correct answer: D

Maxillofacial fractures can potentially cause airway impairment. Assessing airway is more important than any other assessment answer choice. Other fractures that can impact airway include the clavicles, scapulae, ribs, and sternum.

A is incorrect because pain assessment is not priority over airway.

B is incorrect because vital signs are important but not priority. The nurse must assess for a patent airway, good oxygenation, and the presence of bilateral lung sounds. Once airway assessment is completed, vital signs should be measured.

C is incorrect because bone displacement will be assessed after the patient is determined to be stable.

38. A patient tells the nurse they are always tired upon waking, despite getting eight hours of sleep. What is the first action the nurse should take?

    A. Contact the provider for a prescription for sleep medication.
    B. Tell the patient not to drink beverages with caffeine before bed.
    C. Educate the patient to sleep upright in a reclining chair.
    D. Ask the patient if they have ever been evaluated for sleep apnea.

Rationale:

Correct answer: D

Sleep apnea interrupts normal breathing patterns during sleep, preventing the patient from getting a full night's rest, despite being in bed for eight hours. Many times, patients are not even aware of having sleep apnea. Persistently awaking tired is one of the classic symptoms of sleep apnea. Other conditions to evaluate for include depression, restless leg syndrome, and narcolepsy.

A is incorrect because the cause should be identified first.

B is incorrect because the nurse should not assume that the patient drinks caffeine before bed.

C is incorrect because sleeping in a chair is priority for someone with difficulty breathing while sleeping. This has not been identified in this patient.

39. A patient with a paralyzed vocal cord is educated by the nurse. For aspiration prevention, what technique does the nurse teach?

    A. Tilt the head back as far as possible when swallowing

    B. Tuck the chin down when swallowing

    C. Breathe slowly and deeply while swallowing

    D. Keep the head very still and straight while swallowing

Rationale:

Correct answer: B

Patients who have paralyzed vocal cords in the open position are at risk for aspiration. Tucking in the chin when swallowing will prevent aspiration.

A is incorrect because tilting the head back increases risk of aspiration.

C is incorrect because breathing slowly does not decrease risk of aspiration.

D is incorrect because limiting movement does not decrease risk of aspiration.

40. The nurse is assessing four patients on the medical-surgical unit. Which of the following patients does the nurse place at greatest risk for obstructive sleep apnea?

    A. 19-year-old who is eight months pregnant

    B. 65-year-old with gastroesophageal reflux disease (GERD)

    C. 42-year-old who is 60 pounds overweight

    D. 75-year-old with type 2 diabetes mellitus

Rationale:

Correct answer: C

Obstructive sleep apnea is closure of the airway when sleeping due to excess weight and tissue. The patient at highest risk is overweight. The risk for sleep apnea is also higher in men with a neck circumference of 17 inches or more (16 inches or more for women) because a large neck has more soft tissue that can block the airway during sleep. Sleep apnea is more common between young adulthood and middle age and more common in men than women. Women's risk for sleep apnea increases with menopause.

A is incorrect because pregnancy is not a risk for obstructive sleep apnea.

B is incorrect because GERD is not a risk for obstructive sleep apnea.

D is incorrect because diabetes is not a risk for obstructive sleep apnea.

NCLEX-RN – MED-SURG: ENDOCRINE – 40 QUESTIONS

1. The nurse on the medical-surgical unit is caring for a patient admitted for aldosterone deficiency. Which of the following assessment findings does the nurse expect to see when caring for this patient?

   A. Vasoconstriction
   B. Serum sodium 146 mEq/L
   C. Increased urine output
   D. Blood glucose 96 mg/dL

   Rationale:

   Correct answer: C

   Aldosterone is a mineralocorticoid which maintains extracellular fluid volume. Its action stimulates reabsorption of sodium and water and excretion of potassium in the tubules of the kidney. The patient with aldosterone deficiency would, therefore, have increased urine output with sodium loss and potassium retention.

   A is incorrect because vasoconstriction is not an effect of aldosterone.

   B is incorrect because in aldosterone deficiency, the sodium level would be decreased.

   D is incorrect because aldosterone does not affect blood glucose.

2. A female patient on the medical unit is admitted with decreased adrenal function. Which of the following patient statements does the nurse expect when talking with a patient with decreased adrenal function?

   A. "I've been craving potato chips."

B. "My face seems to be changing, and I feel like I am starting to look like a man."

C. "I'm always hungry, even after eating."

D. "I've taken extra hormone replacement recently, and I still feel moody."

Rationale:

Correct answer: A

Decreased adrenal function is correlated with cravings for salt. The adrenal glands are responsible for producing hormones that maintain blood pressure, regulate metabolism, and slow the immune response. Lack of these hormones leads to sodium and water wasting and potassium retention. Other symptoms include dehydration, decreased blood pressure, weight loss, alopecia, fatigue, depression, lethargy, and pathological fractures.

B is incorrect because masculinization in females is a characteristic of increased adrenal hormone secretion (Cushing's), not decreased adrenal function.

C is incorrect because hunger despite eating correlates with diabetes.

D is incorrect because although synthetic adrenal hormones may cause moodiness, the nurse should not expect the patient to be doubling the dose. Too much hormone replacement can cause symptoms of Cushing's, such as excessive mood swings.

3. A patient is scheduled for a serum catecholamine test. When the nurse is collecting the sample, which is the priority action by the nurse?

   A. Draw the blood after breakfast

   B. Immediately send the blood to the lab after placing on ice

   C. Add preservatives to the specimen before sending to the lab

   D. Discard the first blood sample then collect the specimen

Rationale:

Correct answer: B

A serum catecholamine test measures epinephrine, dopamine, and norepinephrine, which are all hormones found in the blood made by the adrenal glands. This test assists in diagnosing catecholamine-secreting tumors, such as those found in the adrenal medulla, and in the investigation of hypertension and pheochromocytoma. The blood specimen for a serum catecholamine test needs to be placed on ice and sent to the lab immediately.

A is incorrect because the patient should not eat for several hours before the sample is drawn.

C is incorrect because the correct blood collection tube will have the appropriate preservatives already.

D is incorrect because the first blood sample should not be discarded.

4. A patient in the clinic has a 24-hour urine collection ordered for hormone excretion. When the patient asks the nurse why the urine needs to be collected for 24 hours instead of random, what is the best response by the nurse?

    A. "The 24-hour sample will assess your circadian rhythm hormones."
    B. "Hormones are dilute in urine, so a large volume is needed."
    C. "You need to urinate multiple times for collection of the correct hormone."
    D. "We will be evaluating urine every three hours for 24 hours to determine when certain hormones are secreted in larger amounts."

Rationale:

Correct answer: A

Certain hormones are secreted according to a circadian rhythm. The 24-hour urine collection is the most accurate reflection of hormone secretion.

B is incorrect because hormone dilution in urine is not an indication for a 24-hour urine collection.

C is incorrect because collecting the correct hormone is not an indication for a 24-hour urine collection.

D is incorrect because a 24-hour urine specimen is collected over a full 24-hour period and then sent to the lab at one time.

5. A male patient in the clinic reports fluid secretion from the breasts. When the nurse evaluates the results of this patient's blood tests, which hormone value would be assessed first?

A. Posterior pituitary hormone

B. Adrenal medulla hormone

C. Anterior pituitary hormone

D. Parathyroid hormone

Rationale:

Correct answer: C

Prolactin is the hormone responsible for fluid and milk production from the breast, and this hormone is secreted by the anterior pituitary gland.

A is incorrect because the posterior pituitary stores and releases oxytocin and vasopressin.

B is incorrect because the adrenal medulla converts tyrosine into epinephrine, norepinephrine, and dopamine.

D is incorrect because parathyroid hormone is secreted from parathyroid glands and is important for bone remodeling.

6. The nurse on the medical-surgical unit is caring for a patient admitted for excessive calcitonin. Which electrolyte imbalance does the nurse assess the patient for?

A. Hyperkalemia

B. Decreased sodium

C. Decreased calcium

D. Hypercalcemia

Rationale:

Correct answer: C

Calcitonin is produced by parafollicular cells of the parathyroid gland. This serves the purpose of reducing serum calcium levels, or preventing hypercalcemia.

A is incorrect because calcitonin has no effect on potassium.

B is incorrect because calcitonin has no effect on sodium.

D is incorrect because calcitonin does not cause increased serum calcium. Parathyroid hormone increases calcium levels.

7. A patient in the clinic has been taking a prescribed beta1 receptor stimulator. When the nurse assesses the patient, which finding would necessitate notifying the healthcare provider immediately?

    A. Heart rate 55 bpm
    B. Respiratory rate 16 bpm
    C. Pulse ox 93%
    D. Blood pressure 140/72 mmHg

Rationale:

Correct answer: A

The heart has beta1 receptor sites, which, when stimulated, will have positive chronotropic and positive inotropic effects. The patient should have an increased heart rate and strengthened contractility, thus a greater cardiac output. The decreased heart rate indicates the patient is not responding in the expected manner to the medication.

B is incorrect because this is a normal respiratory rate, and this medication would have no effect on breathing.

C is incorrect because the medication would have no effect on oxygenation. Because this SpO₂ is low, the nurse should further assess the patient and consider instructing the patient to cough and deep breathe or apply oxygen by nasal cannula. If the oxygen level does not rise in response to nursing interventions, the healthcare provider may need to be notified.

D is incorrect because the blood pressure is slightly elevated but not a primary concern. The nurse should continue to monitor blood pressure, give PRN antihypertensive medications, if ordered, and notify the healthcare provider if the hypertension worsens.

8. The nurse on the medical-surgical unit is assessing four patients. Which of the following patients are at the greatest risk for gonadotropin and growth hormone deficiency?

    A. 32-year-old female on long term oral contraceptives
    B. 45-year-old male with a history of head trauma four years ago
    C. 56-year-old female allergic to shellfish
    D. 43-year-old male with diabetes mellitus

Rationale:

Correct answer: B

Head trauma can cause hypofunction of the anterior pituitary gland. This may lead to deficiency of gonadotropin and growth hormone.

A is incorrect because contraceptives do not increase risk for gonadotropin and growth hormone deficiency. Oral contraceptives increase the risk for breast cancer.

C is incorrect because shellfish allergy does not increase risk for gonadotropin and growth hormone deficiency. Allergy to shellfish (which is high in iodine) poses a risk for a client who undergoes a dye-containing procedure, since most dyes used in diagnostic procedures contain iodine.

D is incorrect because diabetes mellitus does not increase risk for gonadotropin and growth hormone deficiency.

9. A patient with acromegaly has been educated by the nurse regarding an upcoming hypophysectomy procedure. Which of the following patient statements demonstrates more teaching is needed?

    A. "I won't need to limit fluid intake after the surgery."
    B. "I'm glad I won't have a visible incision."
    C. "I hope my shoe size will go back down."
    D. "I will wear my house slippers so I don't have to bend over to put shoes on."

Rationale:

Correct answer: C

Acromegaly occurs as a result of excessive growth hormone secretion from the pituitary gland, which causes enlarged body size: hands, feet, forehead, nose, and jaw. Other symptoms include poor coordination, deep voice, sexual abnormalities, and visual field changes. Growth hormone is secreted by the anterior pituitary gland, and a hypophysectomy is performed to remove the portion of the gland or a tumor that is causing excessive secretion of the hormone. After the surgery, many of the symptoms of hyperpituitarism are relieved, but skeletal changes as well as organ enlargement will not generally reverse.

A is incorrect because the statement indicates the client understands the teaching about post-op expectations. Fluid intake should be encouraged after the patient has recovered from the anesthesia after a hypophysectomy surgery.

B is incorrect as this statement indicates understanding because the incision from hypophysectomy is not visible.

D is incorrect because the statement indicates the client understands to avoid bending over after the hypophysectomy.

10. A female patient is in the clinic complaining of body image concerns regarding hirsutism. When assessing this patient, the nurse should ask which of the following questions?

    A. "How do you plan to cover the medical bills for your treatments?"
    B. "How do you feel when you look in the mirror?"
    C. "What are your prescribed medications?"
    D. "What measures have you taken to handle this problem?"

Rationale:

Correct answer: B

Hirsutism is excessive hair growth that occurs on the face and body as a result of endocrine disorder. Especially in female patients, this causes disruption of body image. Self-perception and body image feelings of the patient should be assessed by the nurse.

A is incorrect because financial status does not address the patient's presenting physical problem. The nurse should remain focused on the client's here-and-now physical needs as a priority.

C is incorrect because current medications do not address the patient's presenting problem. Assessment of current medications is certainly an important component of the nursing assessment, but this assessment is not directly related to the body image concerns the patient is expressing.

D is incorrect because hirsutism is not caused by any specific behaviors, and it cannot be prevented totally. Some patients may shave, wax, or use other methods for hair removal, but assessing how the patient currently feels is more important than determining past attempts to deal with the problem.

11. The nurse is caring for a 68-year-old female patient and is providing education regarding decreased estrogen production. In order to decrease risk of injury, which statement does the nurse include?

    A. "Drink up to two liters of water daily to prevent falls and accidental fractures."
    B. "Daily exercise, such as a walk around your neighborhood, will help prevent injury."
    C. "Bathe the perineum two times a day."
    D. "Check your blood sugar daily so you don't experience dizziness related to hypoglycemia."

Rationale:

Correct answer: B

Older female patients, who have decreased estrogen production, are at risk for bone density reduction as well as fractures. Daily exercise, such as walking around the neighborhood, should be encouraged by the nurse.

A is incorrect because adequate fluid intake will decrease vaginal dryness associated with decreased estrogen production but will not prevent injury. Normal daily fluid intake for average adults is 2-2.5 liters daily.

C is incorrect because perineal care will decrease vaginal dryness, but not prevent injury.

D is incorrect because abnormal blood glucose levels are not related to decreased estrogen production in older age. A 68-year-old client does not need to check blood glucose regularly unless indicated by a specific diagnosis such as diabetes.

12. The nurse on the medical unit is assessing a patient who takes levothyroxine for hypothyroidism. Which of the following findings indicates the medication is effective?

    A. The patient recognizes thirst and is drinking fluids
    B. The patient's weight has increased 1 pound the past three weeks
    C. The patient's white blood cell count is 7,000 cells/mm3
    D. The patient's heart rate is 68 bpm

Rationale:

Correct answer: D

Hypothyroidism is decreased activity of the thyroid gland, which decreases body functioning. Symptoms of hypothyroidism include bradycardia, confusion, alopecia, dry skin and hair, and constipation. The patient's heart rate is normal at 68 which indicates the medication is working. If the dose of thyroid hormone replacement medication were too high, the heart rate would be elevated.

A is incorrect because thirst does not indicate therapeutic response to levothyroxine.

B is incorrect because patients with hypothyroidism tend to experience weight gain and obesity. Gaining a pound in three weeks is not an indication of effectiveness of levothyroxine. Weight loss (over time) would be a sign of improvement with this medication.

C is incorrect because decreased white blood cell count is not an intended effect of levothyroxine.

13. The nurse in the clinic is assessing four patients for potential endocrine disorder. Which patient does the nurse identify as being at the greatest risk of hyperparathyroidism?

    A. 28-year-old female who has pregnancy induced hypertension
    B. 43-year-old male on dialysis for end stage kidney disease
    C. 62-year-old female diagnosed with heart failure
    D. 75-year-old male with asthma and hypertension who uses oxygen at home

Rationale:

Correct answer: B

Hyperparathyroidism can be a result of disorders that cause hypocalcemia. Patients with chronic kidney disease cannot activate vitamin D and have poor absorption of calcium in the gastrointestinal tract. This puts the patient at highest risk for hyperparathyroidism.

A is incorrect because pregnancy-induced hypertension does not increase risk of hyperparathyroidism. Pregnancy-induced hypertension can cause thrombocytopenia, HELLP syndrome, and if it progresses to eclampsia, ultimately renal failure and cerebral hemorrhage.

C is incorrect because heart failure does not increase risk of hyperparathyroidism. Patients with heart failure are at risk for liver failure, atrial fibrillation, and other arrhythmias.

D is incorrect because this patient's medical details do not indicate increased risk for hyperparathyroidism.

14. The nurse in the recovery room is caring for a patient who had a transsphenoidal hypophysectomy. What is the priority action the nurse should take?

   A. Keep the patient supine and head of bed flat
   B. Educate the patient regarding turning, coughing, and deep breathing
   C. Monitor for nasal drainage
   D. Prevent dryness of the lips by applying petroleum jelly

Rationale:

Correct answer: C

Hypophysectomy is partial or complete removal of the pituitary gland. Drainage from the nose after hypophysectomy, especially light yellow or halo effect, would indicate leaking of cerebrospinal fluid. The healthcare provider should be notified of this finding immediately.

A is incorrect because the patient should have the head of bed elevated after hypophysectomy.

B is incorrect because the patient should not be coughing postoperatively as this can increase the risk for a CSF leak.

D is incorrect because petroleum jelly can be applied to the lips, but this is not as important as drainage from the nose.

15. A patient is admitted to the medical-surgical unit for excessive catecholamine release. Which of the following assessment findings does the nurse correlate with the patient's diagnosis?

   A. Blood pressure 110/72 mmHg
   B. Pulse 112 beats per minute
   C. Respirations 8 per minute
   D. Urine output 200 ml/hour

Rationale:

Correct answer: B

Catecholamines, or epinephrine and norepinephrine, are released from the adrenal medulla of the adrenal glands when the sympathetic nervous system is activated. This is part of the fight or flight stress response. Characteristic findings include an increased pulse, increased blood pressure, and increased blood glucose.

A is incorrect because catecholamines increase blood pressure.

C is incorrect because catecholamines increase respirations.

D is incorrect because catecholamines do not increase urine output. Normal urine output is 30-60 ml/hr.

16. The nurse is caring for an adult patient hospitalized for an upper respiratory tract infection (URI) and a history of growth hormone deficiency. Which of the following actions should the nurse include?

    A. Avoid subcutaneous injections
    B. Put the patient in isolation
    C. Reposition the patient with a lift sheet
    D. Have the patient dangle the lower extremities before standing

Rationale:

Correct answer: C

Growth hormone helps maintain bone strength and density, so patients with growth hormone deficiency (hypopituitarism, or dwarfism) often have fragile, thin bones. A lift sheet is a safety measure to prevent fractures when repositioning in the bed.

A is incorrect because avoiding subcutaneous injections is not a safety measure for a patient with growth hormone deficiency. Some patients with human growth hormone deficiency are treated routinely with subcutaneous human chorionic gonadotropin (HcG) injections.

B is incorrect because isolation is not necessary for a patient with growth hormone deficiency. A patient with an URI can share a semi-private room with another patient infected with the same bacteria or can be placed in a private room, but isolation is not necessary.

D is incorrect because having the patient dangle the lower extremities before standing is not a necessary safety measure for a patient with growth hormone deficiency.

17. The nurse is caring for a patient recovering after endoscopic trans-nasal hypophysectomy. When the nurse teaches the patient regarding the procedure, which patient statement demonstrates correct understanding?

    A. "I will wear sunglasses to decrease sun exposure."
    B. "I will keep food in upper cabinets to prevent having to bend over."
    C. "I will wash my incision daily with half-strength hydrogen peroxide and apply a new dressing."
    D. "While awake, I will cough and deep breathe every two hours."

Rationale:

Correct answer: B

Endoscopic trans-nasal hypophysectomy is performed to remove the portion of the gland or a tumor that is causing excessive secretion of growth hormone. Following the surgery, the patient is advised to avoid bending over and any other activities that may increase intracranial pressure. Other important components of post-hypophysectomy nursing care include monitor I/O, observe for hypoglycemia, check neurological status frequently, and teach the client to avoid toothbrushing for two weeks.

A is incorrect because decreasing sun exposure is not necessary after endoscopic trans-nasal hypophysectomy.

C is incorrect because there is no visible incision with endoscopic trans-nasal hypophysectomy.

D is incorrect because coughing and deep breathing will increase intracranial pressure, which is not desired after this surgical procedure.

18. A 72-year-old patient is admitted to the medical unit for pneumonia. The patient has no significant health history and no known allergies. When planning this patient's care, which of the following should the nurse include?

    A. Airborne precautions
    B. PO fluids every 1-2 hours
    C. Indwelling urinary catheter
    D. Palpate thyroid gland

Rationale:

Correct answer: B

Older adults can experience decreased antidiuretic hormone (ADH) production as a normal part of the aging process. Decreased ADH leads to dilute urine with excessive fluid loss, which can lead to dehydration. The patient should be offered PO fluids every 1-2 hours and fluid intake should be encouraged up to 3L daily with pneumonia.

A is incorrect because pneumonia is not an indication for airborne precautions. Airborne precautions are required for tuberculosis, active varicella, rubeola, and disseminated zoster (shingles).

C is incorrect because although assessing I&O is necessary, an indwelling urinary catheter is not indicated for a diagnosis of pneumonia.

D is incorrect because assessing the thyroid gland is not indicated.

19. A patient is prescribed spironolactone before surgery for hyperaldosteronism. The nurse will teach the patient about which precautions?

    A. "Read labels of salt substitutes."
    B. "Don't add salt to food."
    C. "Avoid the sun."
    D. "Take acetaminophen for pain, not aspirin."

Rationale:

Correct answer: A

Salt substitutes frequently contain potassium and using spironolactone can lead to hyperkalemia as it is a potassium-sparing diuretic. Use of spironolactone is indicated to maintain or increase potassium levels and use of salt substitutes can be dangerous.

B is incorrect because spironolactone can cause hyponatremia and hyperkalemia, and avoiding salt is not necessary.

C is incorrect because spironolactone does not cause photosensitivity, so avoiding the sun is not necessary.

D is incorrect because avoiding aspirin is not necessary.

20. The nurse in the clinic needs to assess a patient's thyroid gland. When palpating the thyroid, which action should the nurse take?

   A. Face the patient to palpate the thyroid gland
   B. Have the patient swallow after palpation
   C. Palpate the right lobe of the thyroid gland with the left hand
   D. Have the patient sit with the chin tucked downward

Rationale:

Correct answer: D

The nurse has the patient sit down and tuck their chin downward and stands behind the patient to palpate the thyroid gland.

A is incorrect because the proper technique for palpating the thyroid gland is standing behind the patient.

B is incorrect because the proper way to assess the thyroid gland is to palpate while the patient swallows.

C is incorrect because the nurse palpates the right side for the isthmus while the patient swallows and turns the head to the right.

21. The nurse is caring for a patient on the medical unit. Which patient statement would alert the nurse that the patient may have hypothyroidism?

   A. "My sister has problems with her thyroid."
   B. "I'm much more sensitive to heat than others."
   C. "I have to add quite a bit of salt to my food to make it taste good."
   D. "I could sleep 12 hours and still be tired."

Rationale:

Correct answer: D

Hypothyroidism is characterized by decreased production of thyroid hormone and happens more often in older adult females. Feeling tired after adequate sleep is common in hypothyroidism. Other symptoms include decreased activity level, weight gain, constipation, alopecia, bradycardia, and decreased ability to perspire.

A is incorrect because hypothyroidism is not genetic or inherited.

B is incorrect because hypothyroidism causes intolerance to cold. Hyperthyroidism causes sensitivity to heat.

C is incorrect because taste loss is not indicative of hypothyroidism.

22. A patient is admitted to the medical-surgical unit with a diagnosis of Hashimoto's thyroiditis and hypothyroidism. When the patient asks the nurse how long the thyroid medication will need to be taken, what is the best response by the nurse?

   A. "The medication will need to be taken until the goiter is gone completely."
   B. "Thyroiditis is cured by treatment with antibiotics. Once that is resolved you won't require thyroid medication."
   C. "Your thyroid will not work again, so you will take thyroid replacement for the rest of your life."
   D. "We will test your thyroid function with blood tests, and when your thyroid function returns to normal, the medication can be stopped."

Rationale:

Correct answer: C

Hashimoto's thyroiditis or Hashimoto's disease is the result of an autoimmune process. The immune system attacks and damages the thyroid which leads to hypothyroidism. Thyroid function is permanently lost, so lifelong thyroid replacement therapy is necessary.

A is incorrect because even if the goiter is reduced or eliminated, the patient cannot stop taking the thyroid medication.

B is incorrect because antibiotics will not cure the thyroiditis and the patient cannot stop taking the thyroid medication.

D is incorrect because the patient cannot stop taking the thyroid medication.

23. The nurse on the medical unit is caring for a child newly diagnosed with Graves' disease. How should the nurse respond when the patient's mother asks, "Is my daughter's new diagnosis disease due to my type 1 diabetes?"

A. "Your diabetes did not cause your daughter's Graves' disease. There is no known connection between diabetes and Graves' disease."

B. "There is a connection between diabetes and Graves' disease, but your diabetes did not likely cause your daughter's Graves' disease."

C. "There is an association between Graves' disease and autoimmune diseases such as rheumatoid arthritis, but not with diabetes."

D. "Diabetes can cause hypothyroidism, so yes, that is a possibility."

Rationale:

Correct answer: B

Graves' disease is over-activity of the thyroid gland as a whole, or hyperthyroidism. Also, termed "toxic diffuse goiter," it is the result of an autoimmune process with symptoms including sleeping problems, tachycardia, poor heat tolerance, irritability, and exophthalmos. Research shows an association between Graves' disease and other autoimmune diseases, such as type 1 diabetes, but predisposition is most likely polygenic and not caused by the mother's diabetes.

A is incorrect because there is a known connection between diabetes and Graves' disease.

C is incorrect because there is a known connection between diabetes and Graves' disease.

D is incorrect because diabetes does not cause hypothyroidism, and the daughter has hyperthyroidism, not hypothyroidism.

24. The nurse on the surgical unit is caring for a patient after recovery from complete thyroidectomy. When the nurse is reinforcing postoperative teaching, which of the following patient statements demonstrates more education is needed?

   A. "I might need calcium replacement after this surgery."
   B. "I won't need to take my thyroid medication anymore."
   C. "I will be on thyroid hormones for life."
   D. "If I need it, I can take pain medication."

Rationale:

Correct answer: B

Complete thyroidectomy may be carried out as a primary treatment for thyroid carcinoma hyperthyroidism. Because the thyroid has been removed completely, the patient will need to take thyroid medication for life to return thyroid hormone levels and metabolic rate to normal.

A is incorrect because calcium needs aren't determined until after the patient has been evaluated for parathyroid damage, which is a potential complication after thyroidectomy. If calcium levels fall, the nurse may note hyperirritability of the nerves, twitching hands and feet, and rarely, laryngospasm. The patient's statement indicates that calcium supplementation may be needed.

C is incorrect because the patient will need to take thyroid medication for life, indicating correct understanding.

D is incorrect because the patient can have pain medication after surgery, indicating correct understanding. Managing pain, avoiding stress on suture lines, increasing humidity, and encouraging rest, relaxation, and nutrition are important components of the postoperative care.

25. The nurse is planning care for a patient admitted with hyperparathyroidism. Which of the following interventions does the nurse include?

    A. Keep the patient on bed rest to prevent stress on bones
    B. Encourage PO fluids of 2L/day or more
    C. Brush teeth with a soft toothbrush
    D. Administer thiazide diuretics to prevent fluid volume overload

Rationale:

Correct answer: B

The parathyroid gland controls calcium levels in the blood and bones, and hyperparathyroidism causes resorption of calcium from bones to increase. This puts the patient at risk for renal calculi. Fluids intake of 2L or more daily helps decrease formation of kidney stones. Cranberry juice is suggested because it can lower urinary pH. The patient is instructed to report abdominal pain and hematuria, which are signs of renal calculi.

A is incorrect because bed rest increases calcium excretion and risk for renal calculi. Mobility with the use of a rocking chair or ambulation is encouraged as much as possible because bones subjected to normal stress give up less calcium.

C is incorrect because using a soft toothbrush is not specific to hyperparathyroidism.

D is incorrect because thiazide diuretics are contraindicated in a patient with hyperparathyroidism. These medications decrease renal excretion of calcium and increase the risk for hypercalcemic crisis.

26. The nurse is monitoring a patient after parathyroidectomy. The nurse notes flexion contractions of the patient's hand when the blood pressure is taken. Which of the following lab results would the nurse associate with this finding?

    A. Serum potassium 2.8 mEq/L
    B. Serum magnesium 1.6 mEq/L
    C. Serum sodium 124 mEq/L
    D. Serum calcium 5.7 mg/dL

Rationale:

Correct answer: D

The parathyroid gland controls calcium levels in the blood and bones. Once the parathyroid gland is removed with surgery, hypocalcemia may occur. This leads to muscle twitches, muscle spasms, and tetany. This is worsened if tissue hypoxia is present. Trousseau's sign is carpal spasm when the blood pressure cuff is applied for three minutes, which indicates hypocalcemia. The nurse may also see Chvostek's sign, twitching of the eye, cheek, nose, or mouth when the facial nerve is tapped.

A is incorrect because hypokalemia is not associated with parathyroidectomy.

B is incorrect because hypomagnesemia is not associated with parathyroidectomy.

C is incorrect because hyponatremia is not associated with parathyroidectomy.

27. The nurse on the medical-surgical unit is assessing a patient admitted with Graves' disease. When vital signs are taken, it is noted the temperature has risen by 1°F (0.56°C) in the last hour. What is the first action the nurse should take?

A. Turn down the room lights and shut the door

B. Call for a STAT electrocardiogram (ECG)

C. Calculate apical-radial pulse deficit

D. Administer acetaminophen 650 mg PO

Rationale:

Correct answer: A

Graves' disease is overactive thyroid gland as a whole, or hyperthyroidism. Also termed "toxic diffuse goiter," it is the result of autoimmune disease with symptoms including sleeping problems, tachycardia, poor heat tolerance, irritability, and exophthalmos. The temperature increase could indicate thyroid storm is developing, and the nurse needs to notify the healthcare provider after reducing environmental stimuli which could lead to cardiac complications.

B is incorrect because environmental stimuli need to be minimized first.

C is incorrect because calculating apical-radial pulse deficit is unnecessary.

D is incorrect because acetaminophen is not indicated as thyroid activity is responsible for temperature increase. Acetaminophen may reduce the temperature because it is an antipyretic, but it will not treat the overactive thyroid or prevent thyroid storm.

28. A patient is admitted to the cardiac unit for bradycardia due to hypothyroidism. Which of the following medications does the nurse anticipate administering to this patient?

    A. Atropine sulfate

    B. Levothyroxine sodium

    C. Propranolol

    D. Epinephrine

Rationale:

Correct answer: B

The cause of this patient's bradycardia is hypothyroidism, so the nurse anticipates administering levothyroxine sodium. If the patient becomes symptomatic from the bradycardia, atropine or epinephrine could be administered as short-term treatment.

A is incorrect because atropine sulfate is only indicated if the patient is experiencing symptomatic bradycardia. When bradycardia is present due to hypothyroidism, the initial medication to increase the heartrate is a thyroid replacement medication, such as levothyroxine sodium.

C is incorrect because propranolol is a beta blocker and contraindicated for bradycardia as it will cause a further decrease in the patient's heartrate.

D is incorrect because epinephrine is only indicated if the patient is symptomatic.

29. The nurse on the medical unit is planning care for a patient admitted for hypothyroidism. Which of the following is a priority problem that should be addressed first by the nurse?

    A. Intolerance to heat
    B. Body image problems
    C. Depression and withdrawal
    D. Depressed ventilation

Rationale:

Correct answer: D

Hypothyroid patients may have ineffective breathing patterns related to depressed ventilation. The nurse must monitor respiratory rate, depth, and pattern. Pulse oximetry and arterial blood gases may be used to determine of oxygenation is adequate. Deep breathing, coughing, and incentive spirometry should be encouraged, and sedative medications should be avoided or used with caution.

A is incorrect because intolerance to heat is characteristic of hyperthyroidism, not hypothyroidism.

B is incorrect because body image problems are psychosocial and not a greater priority than other concerns which may have a detrimental physical effect on the patient.

C is incorrect because a depressed respiratory system is a greater priority than psychosocial issues, such as depression and withdrawal. The depressed patient may have a lack of motivation for self-care, but the nurse must address the respiratory system first.

30. A patient on the medical-surgical unit with adrenal hyperfunction screamed at her husband, threw a water pitcher across the room, then started crying uncontrollably. When the patient tells the nurse she feels like she is losing her mind, what is the best response by the nurse?

    A. "I will notify the healthcare provider for a psychiatric consult."
    B. "Your hormone levels are causing this."
    C. "I can bring you some pamphlets regarding support groups."
    D. "I will post a sign on your room restricting visitors and close the door."

Rationale:

Correct answer: B

The adrenal glands are responsible for secreting cortisol, and the patient with adrenal hyperfunction has hypercortisolism. This can lead to changes in mood and mental behavior, psychosis, or neurotic behavior. The patient must be educated about behavior changes that are not psychiatric in nature and which often improve with blood cortisol level stabilization.

A is incorrect because the behavior is not psychiatric in nature.

C is incorrect because providing factual information about the physical changes taking place in the body is more appropriate than support groups.

D is incorrect because restricting visitors is not needed.

31. The nurse on the medical-surgical unit is caring for a patient admitted with pneumonia and a history of hypothyroidism. What is the priority intervention the nurse should include when planning care?

    A. Monitor IV site every shift
    B. Administer acetaminophen for fever
    C. Ensure suction equipment is working
    D. Limit PO fluids to prevent fluid volume overload

Rationale:

Correct answer: C

Patients with hypothyroidism who are diagnosed with another illness such as pneumonia are at risk for myxedema coma. Myxedema coma is severe hypothyroidism that can present with hypothermia, decreased mental status, and decreased respiratory rate, pulse, and blood pressure. This is an emergency situation in which maintaining airway is priority. Suction equipment must be available in the room and checked for function routinely if the patient should develop myxedema coma.

A is incorrect because monitoring IV site is necessary but not priority.

B is incorrect because acetaminophen administration for fever is necessary but not priority.

D is incorrect because PO fluids should be encouraged for the patient with hypothyroidism because they are at increased risk for constipation.

32. The nurse is teaching a patient about a prescription for prednisone for cortisol deficiency. Which of the following statements does the nurse include in the teaching?

    A. "You will need to rotate injection sites."
    B. "You will need another drug if you work in the heat outside."
    C. "Your diet will need strict sodium restrictions."
    D. "Take one pill when you wake up and two pills before bed."

Rationale:

Correct answer: B

Working outside in the heat necessitates adjustment of steroid dosage, as the patient will sweat more than normal.

A is incorrect because prednisone is taken orally for cortisol deficiency.

C is incorrect because sodium restriction is not required when taking prednisone.

D is incorrect because dosage is usually two pills in the morning and one pill at night.

33. A patient with chronic hypercortisolism is admitted to the medical unit. Which of the following actions does the nurse take?

    A. Wash hands upon entering the room
    B. Place patient in airborne isolation

81

C. Observe for signs of infection

D. Assess daily chest X-ray

Rationale:

Correct answer: A

Washing hands when entering patient rooms is always appropriate but specifically for the patient who has hypercortisolism. Increased levels of cortisol will decrease lymphocytes, inhibit macrophage maturation, decrease antibody synthesis, and inhibit cytokine and inflammatory chemical synthesis. This causes increased risk of infection, so handwashing is vital to prevent bringing unwanted bacteria into the patient's room.

B is incorrect because the patient with chronic hypercortisolism does not need airborne isolation.

C is incorrect because the patient will not display the usual signs of infection due to hypercortisolism.

D is incorrect because the patient does not require daily chest X-rays.

34. The nurse is teaching a patient newly diagnosed with diabetes mellitus. When the patient asks why blood glucose levels should be maintained at greater than 60 mg/dL, what is the best response by the nurse?

   A. "Glucose is the only fuel the body uses for energy production."
   B. "The brain constantly requires glucose supply as it is unable to store glucose."
   C. "When minimum blood glucose is not maintained, the body does not produce red blood cells."
   D. "Maintaining blood glucose levels prevents lactic acid buildup and acidosis."

Rationale:

Correct answer: B

The brain does not synthesize or store glucose, so a constant supply from blood circulation is required for meeting central nervous system needs. The patient needs to be taught about maintaining minimum blood glucose to prevent a hypoglycemia prevention.

A is incorrect because fat and protein are also used as fuel by the body.

C is incorrect because red blood cell production and glucose are unrelated. Erythropoietin, a hormone secreted by the kidney, stimulates the production of red blood cells.

D is incorrect because blood glucose levels are not responsible for formation of lactic acid. Insufficient oxygen supply to muscles is the cause of lactic acid formation.

35. The nurse in the emergency room is caring for a patient experiencing acute adrenal crisis. What is the first action the nurse should take?

    A. Start a peripheral IV
    B. Administer hydrocortisone succinate
    C. Check blood glucose
    D. Administer dextrose and insulin

Rationale:

Correct answer: A

Acute adrenal crisis is adrenal insufficiency with decreased levels of cortisol. Signs and symptoms include abdominal pain, confusion, fatigue, hypotension, tachycardia, tachypnea, muscle weakness, dark pigmentation, and high fever. Patients may also experience low serum sodium and hyperkalemia. Therapy for acute adrenal crisis is administered intravenously, so the first action is starting an IV.

B is incorrect because the drug cannot be administered until IV access has been established.

C is incorrect because blood glucose is checked hourly as glucose tends to drop in adrenal crisis but establishing IV access is a greater priority.

D is incorrect because dextrose and insulin are administered for hyperkalemia, which may be present with adrenal crisis, but starting an IV is the greater priority.

36. The emergency room nurse is monitoring a patient with possible syndrome of inappropriate antidiuretic hormone (SIADH). The patient has an IV of 0.9% NaCl running at 100 ml/hr. The lab results reflect a sodium level of 112 mEq/L. What is the first action the nurse should take?

    A. Consult the dietitian regarding dietary sodium supplementation
    B. Restrict fluid intake to 500 mL/day

C. Reposition the patient with a lift sheet

D. Delegate hourly intake and output to the unlicensed assistive personnel (UAP)

Rationale:

Correct answer: B

SIADH is the production of too much antidiuretic hormone from the pituitary gland, leading to small amounts of highly concentrated urine excretion and fluid retention. This will lead to dilutional hyponatremia. Treatment includes removing the underlying cause (lung cancer, brain tumor, central nervous system infection) and fluid restriction. The patient currently has an IV running at 100 ml/hr, which will total 2400 mL/24hrs (this is too high). Fluid must be restricted to 500-600 ml/24hrs with SIADH. Retained water will slowly be excreted through the kidneys and serum sodium will slowly return to normal. Diuretics may also be used.

A is incorrect because supplementation of sodium in the diet is not helpful as it may worsen fluid retention.

C is incorrect because the patient is not at risk for fractures, and a lift sheet does not address sodium needs.

D is incorrect because measuring intake and output is necessary, but the priority action is to reduce fluid intake.

37. A patient is admitted to the medical-surgical unit with Cushing's disease. In order to prevent injury, which action does the nurse include when planning care?

    A. Prepare the client for adrenalectomy
    B. Limit vitamin D to prevent hypercalcemia
    C. Reposition the patient with a lift sheet
    D. Ensure suction equipment is working

Rationale:

Correct answer: C

Cushing's disease leads to increased cortisol levels in the blood, which causes bone demineralization. This condition increases risk of pathologic bone fractures, so the patient should be repositioned with a lift sheet rather than pulling on the patient. A protective environment is necessary to prevent falls, fractures, and injuries to bones and soft tissues. The patient may also require the nurse's assistance with ambulation to prevent bumping into corners of furniture.

A is incorrect because adrenalectomy may be required as a surgical treatment option for Cushing's disease, but this does not address safety needs.

B is incorrect because patients with Cushing's disease specifically need adequate amounts of vitamin D in their diet, along with protein and calcium to minimize muscle wasting and osteoporosis.

D is incorrect because the patient with Cushing's disease doesn't often require suctioning, and this nursing implementation does not prevent injury.

38. The nurse is caring for a patient who has 24-hour urine collection ordered. When delegating this task to the unlicensed assistive personnel (UAP), which statement does the nurse include?

    A. "Document time of the patient's first void of the day and collect the urine specimen for 24 hours."
    B. "Preservatives must be added to the specimen container at the end of 24 hours."
    C. "The collection will start with first void in the morning."
    D. "It is important that no more than one urine collection is missed in the 24 hours."

Rationale:

Correct answer: A

The 24-hour urine collection is the most accurate reflection of hormone secretion. It is appropriate to delegate this task to UAP because it does not require critical thinking. It is performed according to a sequence of steps, and the task does not vary much from one patient situation to another. The nurse is responsible for assuring that the collection process is understood. The collection starts after the first morning void, as the first void is discarded due to length of time in the bladder. The time is documented as start time.

B is incorrect because preservatives should be added at the beginning of collection.

C is incorrect because the first void is discarded.

D is incorrect because for accuracy, all voids must be collected within the 24-hour period.

39. The unlicensed assistive personnel (UAP) reports to the nurse that while collecting a 24-hour urine specimen, some of the urine was splashed on her hand. What is the next action the nurse should take?

    A. Ask the UAP if they washed their hands after the splash
    B. Tell the UAP to complete an incident report
    C. Call the lab and ask about the presence of preservatives in the urine collection container
    D. Have the UAP report to employee health services immediately

Rationale:

Correct answer: A

The priority is to determine if the hands have been washed yet. Standard precautions are in place to protect staff and patients from exposure to contaminated fluids and prevent injury. The UAP may need education on Standard Precautions and the importance of wearing gloves.

B is incorrect because an incident report should be completed after the hands are washed.

C is incorrect because although preservatives used in some 24-hr urine collection containers can cause the skin to burn, the lab can be called after the hands have been washed.

D is incorrect because washing the hands is the priority, and the UAP may not need to report to employee health.

40. A 11-year-old male patient is diagnosed with hypopituitarism and has a new prescription for testosterone replacement therapy. When the patient asks the nurse how long the medication should be taken, what is the best response by the nurse?

    A. "Therapy will be discontinued once your blood testosterone levels return to normal."
    B. "When your voice gets deeper and your beard gets thicker, the dose will be decreased, but you will require medication for life."
    C. "Once your sperm count is within normal, the treatment will not be needed anymore."
    D. "Testosterone levels decrease with age, so your treatment will stop when you reach 50 years of age."

86

Rationale:

Correct answer: B

Hypopituitarism (dwarfism) occurs before puberty and causes height below normal with normal body proportions. Bone and tooth growth can be delayed and sexual maturity may be slow. Testosterone replacement therapy is begun with high dose until the patient achieves virility, then the dosage is decreased. The treatment is taken for life.

A is incorrect because testosterone replacement is not discontinued when blood testosterone levels are normal. Discontinuing the hormone replacement would lead to a drop in serum levels.

C is incorrect because testosterone replacement is not discontinued based on when sperm count is increased.

D is incorrect because testosterone replacement is not discontinued when the patient reaches 50 years of age.

NCLEX-RN – MED-SURG: HEMATOLOGY/IMMUNOLOGY – 40 QUESTIONS

1. The nurse in the clinic is assessing a 72-year-old patient for signs and symptoms of infection. What response by the nurse is best when the patient's temperature is found to be 97.5°F (36.3°C)?

    A. Assess for more specific signs

    B. Reassure the patient that the temperature indicates no infection is present

    C. Document the temperature and tell the patient to return to the clinic if the temperature rises above 100°F (37.7°C)

    D. Request blood cultures

Rationale:

Correct answer: A

Due to natural weakening of the immune system function with age, and decreased thermoregulation ability, a fever may not be present in an elderly patient with an infection. The nurse should assess the patient for further, more specific signs of infection.

B is incorrect because immune system function is decreased, so specific signs of infection should be assessed.

C is incorrect because documentation should not be completed until a more thorough assessment has been made.

D is incorrect because a more thorough assessment should be made prior to obtaining blood cultures.

2. A patient who underwent a liver transplant is beginning treatment with prednisone. Which instruction provided by the nurse is the most important regarding the medication?

   A. "Avoid crowds and sick people."
   B. "If you take over-the-counter medications, check the label for acetaminophen."
   C. "Take the medication exactly as ordered, even if you have a fever."
   D. "There is an increased risk of cancer when taking this medication."

Rationale:

Correct answer: A

Prednisone is a steroid medication taken to prevent transplant organ rejection. It works by depressing cell-mediated immune reactors. The patient should avoid crowds and sick people because the body will have decreased ability to fight off infection while taking prednisone.

B is incorrect because prednisone does not contain acetaminophen, and acetaminophen is not contraindicated when taking prednisone.

C is incorrect because although the medication *should* be taken exactly as ordered, a fever can be a sign of infection and the healthcare should be notified. The patient should also be taught that abrupt withdrawal of prednisone can cause headache, nausea, vomiting, and papilledema. The medication should be taken at evenly-spaced intervals throughout the day.

D is incorrect because prednisone does not carry an increased risk of cancer. Rare adverse effects of prednisone include peptic ulcer, gastric hemorrhage, and psychosis.

3. A patient in the intensive care unit (ICU) is recovering from kidney transplant. When the patient experiences hyperacute rejection and the blood pressure is 105/72, the nurse facilitates which treatment?

   A. Dialysis
   B. Administration of high dose steroids
   C. Monoclonal antibody therapy
   D. Plasmapheresis

Rationale:

Correct answer: A

Nothing stops the process of hyperacute rejection, which can begin minutes to several days after transplantation occurs. The transplanted kidney becomes grossly mottled and cyanotic, and the capsule bulges out due to marked edema. The kidney will not function and will have to be removed. The patient will have to undergo dialysis again.

B is incorrect because steroids are ineffective in hyperacute rejection. Cyclosporine and tacrolimus are often used initially.

C is incorrect because monoclonal antibody therapy is ineffective in hyperacute rejection.

D is incorrect because plasmapheresis can only be used in hyperacute rejection if the patient is hemodynamically stable; this patient is hypotensive.

4.   The community health nurse in the clinic is teaching older patients about infection prevention. The nurse knows which of the following is crucial for infection prevention in this population?

   A. Reviewing vaccination records
   B. Encouraging a healthy diet
   C. Proper care of minor wounds
   D. Hand hygiene

Rationale:

Correct answer: A

As people age, the efficiency of the immune system decreases, along with antibodies produced due to past exposure. Older adults will need booster shots for previously administered vaccinations, so the nurse should review vaccination records for this. Diseases that can be prevented in the elderly by administering boosters include shingles, diphtheria, tetanus, pertussis, and pneumonia. Elderly patients should also be encouraged to receive their annual influenza vaccine.

B is incorrect because healthy diet is necessary for all ages and is not as specific to infection prevention as vaccinations.

C is incorrect because the risk for infection in the elderly related to wound infection is not as great as the risk for infection from non-vaccination.

D is incorrect because poor hand hygiene is the leading cause of hospital-acquired infection but not specific to infection prevention in older adults in the community setting.

5. A 65-year-old patient is in the clinic complaining of night sweats and a productive cough. The nurse notes a low fever. The tuberculin skin test is negative. What is the best action for the nurse to do?

   A. Recommend pneumonia vaccination
   B. Teach about viral infections
   C. Recommend rest and fluids
   D. Obtain a chest X-ray

Rationale:

Correct answer: D

T lymphocytes decrease in number with age. This can cause a tuberculin skin test to come back falsely negative. Because the patient has signs and symptoms consistent with tuberculosis (TB), the patient should undergo a chest X-ray for further diagnosis.

A is incorrect because the pneumonia vaccination is not appropriate for anyone who is moderately to severely ill. The pneumococcal pneumonia (PPSV) vaccine should be administered after the patient's current illness has been treated.

B is incorrect because this patient is showing signs of TB, which is a bacterial infection, not a virus.

C is incorrect because although rest and fluids are components of TB treatment, further assessment is more important at this time.

6. The nurse is caring for patients on the medical-surgical unit and using specific practices for prevention of acquisition of human immune deficiency virus (HIV). Which practice by the nurse is the most effective?

   A. Standard precautions used consistently
   B. Double gloves with potential body fluid exposure

C. Label patient charts and armbands with HIV+

D. Wear a mask when near the patient

Rationale:

Correct answer: A

Standard precautions are the primary strategy for infection control in all settings and should be used for all patients. This is the best way to prevent transmission of infectious organisms. Standard precautions apply to contact with blood, body fluids, non-intact skin, and mucous membranes from all patients. The Joint Commission has stated HIV exposure prevention is most effective with Standard Precautions used consistently. HIV does not require the use of droplet, airborne, or contact precautions.

B is incorrect because double gloves are not necessary for bedside patient care. Double gloving is practiced during surgical procedures due to the increased risk of glove penetration with surgical instruments.

C is incorrect because labeling the patient's chart and armband with HIV+ violates the Health Information Portability and Accountability Act (HIPAA).

D is incorrect because a mask is only necessary with airborne precautions. HIV is not spread via the airborne route.

7. The nurse in the clinic is speaking with a patient who just received a negative result for the enzyme-linked immunosorbent assay (ELISA) for HIV. The patient tells the nurse they were worried about getting the results. What is the most important action by the nurse?

    A. Assess sexual activity and patterns
    B. Reassure the patient
    C. Educate the patient regarding safe sex practices
    D. Schedule the patient for another ELISA test in three months

Rationale:

Correct answer: A

The ELISA tests for antibodies for human immune deficiency virus (HIV). Falsely negative ELISA tests can occur after exposure but before antibodies are produced by the immune system. It can take up to 36 months for the antibodies to be produced to get a positive test result. The patient's sexual behavior and patterns need to be assessed in relation to the negative test result and risk for exposure. If the patient knows they have been sexually active with another HIV positive individual, further testing may be warranted at this time.

B is incorrect because the nurse should be cautious to not provide false reassurance. This patient could be infected with HIV even though the preliminary ELISA test is negative.

C is incorrect because education regarding safe sex practices is appropriate, but if the patient has been exposed, further testing is more important that patient education.

D is incorrect because a follow-up ELISA test may be appropriate, but it is more important to focus on the here and now. A Western blot test may be done sooner than three months from now to determine the presence of HIV. The Western blot test has a higher sensitivity to the presence of HIV in the blood.

8. A patient in the clinic is distraught over a recent diagnosis of human immune deficiency virus (HIV). When the patient tells the nurse they don't know what to do, what is the best intervention by the nurse?

    A. Assess for support systems
    B. Offer clergy assistance
    C. Explain requirements by law to inform sex partners
    D. Offer to inform the patient's family

Rationale:

Correct answer: A

The patient is in great need of support systems for assistance. The nurse can help identify the patient's support systems and how they can help.

B is incorrect because the patient may not welcome a clergy member. The nurse should remain focused on nurse-specific activities that can help the patient, and clergy can be called secondarily.

C is incorrect because laws regarding HIV are different in each state and addressing the patient's distress is more important at this time.

D is incorrect because informing the family for the patient is enabling behavior. The nurse should remain focused on the patient and determine coping abilities and support systems before addressing the need to tell the family. It is the patient's choice if and when to inform the family of the diagnosis.

9. A patient with a history of HIV is admitted to the medical unit for pneumonia. The healthcare provider has ordered the addition of several medications to the patient's current regimen. What is the most important action by the nurse?

   A. Consult with the pharmacy regarding drug interactions
   B. Ensure patient understanding of new medications
   C. Administer new medications as well as current medications
   D. Schedule administrations at normal times

Rationale:

Correct answer: A

Medications for HIV/AIDS are complex and are given at specific times throughout the day. This could lead to drug interactions with the new medications ordered by the healthcare provider, so the pharmacy should be consulted about interactions. This is the safest answer choice.

B is incorrect because patient understanding of medications is appropriate but does not provide for patient safety.

C is incorrect because administration of medications without awareness of interactions could be dangerous for the patient.

D is incorrect because HIV/AIDS medications must be administered at specific times. Zidovudine, for example, requires strict adherence to dosage schedule, and didanosine must be taken on an empty stomach.

10. A patient is admitted to the emergency room in sickle cell crisis. Which of the following lab results should be reported to the healthcare provider by the nurse?

   A. Creatinine 2.8 mg/dL
   B. Hematocrit 31%

C. Sodium 148 mEq/L

D. White blood cells 11,500/mm3

Rationale:

Correct answer: A

Sickle cell disease is abnormal formation of red blood cells into a sickle shape, which makes it difficult for them to absorb and transport oxygen through the bloodstream. This leads to fatigue, difficulty breathing, severe pain, joint swelling, jaundice, tachycardia, and low hemoglobin. Organ damage may result, too. Kidney damage is indicated by elevated creatinine levels, which can occur in patients with sickle cell disease. Normal adult creatinine for is 0.7-1.4 mg/dl. Normal child creatinine is 0.4-1.2 mg/dl.

B is incorrect because decreased hematocrit is expected with sickle cell disease. Hematocrit measures the percentage of red blood cells per fluid volume of blood. Normal hematocrit is 42-52% for men, 35-47% for women, and 35-45% for children.

C is incorrect because the sodium is slightly elevated, which can indicate dehydration, but this is not the main concern. Normal sodium is 135-145 mEq/L.

D is incorrect because the white blood cell count is slightly elevated, which could indicate infection, but the creatinine is extremely high, so the patient needs to be evaluated for organ failure ahead of potential infection. Normal adult WBC is 4,500-11,000/mm3. Normal child WBC is 5,000-13,000/mm3.

11. The nurse on the medical-surgical unit is assigned to four patients with immune disorders. Once the hand-off report is received, which of the following patients should be seen by the nurse first?

    A. Patient with AIDS and CD+4 count 200/mm3, temperature 102.1°F (38.8°C)

    B. Patient admitted for Bruton's agammaglonulinemia awaiting discharge teaching

    C. Patient with hypogammaglobulinemia who received immune serum globulin infusion an hour ago

    D. Patient admitted for pneumonia with selective immunoglobulin A deficiency receiving IV antibiotics

Rationale:

Correct answer: A

Patients who are immunosuppressed with high fevers need to be assessed by the nurse first. The patient's immune system is not able to fight infection as well due to decreased CD+4 count, and the high fever can lead to vascular collapse as well as possibly sepsis, which could be fatal. AIDS patients are at risk for opportunistic infections such as *P. jiroveci* (*P. carinii*) pneumonia, *C. albicans* esophagitis or stomatitis, *C. neoformans* meningitis, cytomegalovirus, and Kaposi's sarcoma.

B is incorrect because discharge teaching could be delegated to another nurse so the critical patient can be seen.

C is incorrect because the patient should have vital signs taken after completion of the immune serum globulin infusion, but there is no current indication of a complication and taking vitals can be delegated to another member of the nursing team.

D is incorrect because the patient with selective immunoglobulin A deficiency is stable and can be seen later.

12. A patient is admitted to the emergency room for sickle cell crisis. The patient is dehydrated, and the nurse is planning for IV fluid therapy. Which of the following fluids is the best choice for this patient?

    A. D_5W
    B. 3% sodium
    C. Dextrose 50% (D_{50})
    D. Lactated Ringer's solution

Rationale:

Correct answer: A

Sickle cell disease is abnormal formation of red blood cells into a sickle shape. The red blood cells have difficulty transporting oxygen through the bloodstream, causing fatigue, difficulty breathing, severe pain, joint swelling, jaundice, tachycardia, and low hemoglobin. Dehydration is often present when a patient is in sickle cell crisis. Oral hydration must be promoted in sickling crisis, however, sometimes IV hydration is necessary to treat the dehydration and prevent further sickling of cells. The choice fluid for this situation is D_5W or D_5 in 0.25% NS. Supplemental oxygen may also be needed.

B is incorrect because 3% sodium is a hypertonic solution used to treat patients who are hyponatremic. The sickle cell crisis patent needs D_5W to replace fluid loss from dehydration and provide additional glucose to cells.

C is incorrect because D_{50} is very hypertonic and is used to treat a patient who is hypoglycemic, not dehydrated.

D is incorrect because Lactated Ringer's is an isotonic solution which is safe to use during sickle cell crisis but doesn't provide the needed glucose as does D_5W.

13. A patient who is allergic to bee stings receives a new prescription for an epinephrine auto-injector. After educating the patient regarding the EpiPen, which statement demonstrates more teaching is necessary?

    A. "If symptoms subside, after using my EpiPen, I don't have to come to the emergency room."
    B. "I will have two EpiPens in my purse all the time."
    C. "The expiration date should be written on the calendar."
    D. "I can inject the EpiPen through my clothing."

Rationale:

Correct answer: A

EpiPen is used in severe allergic reactions or anaphylaxis to counteract the massive vasodilation and subsequent hypotension that occurs. Epinephrine causes bronchodilation and reduces mucosal edema to relieve bronchoconstriction and improve respiratory effort. After use of an EpiPen, patients should call 911 or go to the emergency room to be monitored.

B is incorrect because having two EpiPens at all times is good practice and indicates understanding. In the event that one pen is ineffective, faulty, or another dose is needed, it is beneficial to have another pen available.

C is incorrect because the statement indicates understanding. EpiPens have an expiration date, which is important to note on the calendar. Even if the EpiPen hasn't been used, if it becomes expired, it should be disposed of appropriately and a new pen should be obtained.

D is incorrect because it indicates understanding. The EpiPen can be injected through clothing. It is safer to inject through clothing than to postpone the medication's beneficial effects by waiting for clothing removal.

14. The preoperative nurse assesses a patient prior to a spinal laminectomy surgical procedure. The nurse notes the patient is allergic to strawberries and avocados. What is the best action by the nurse?

    A. Assess that the patient has been NPO prior to surgery
    B. Communicate this information with dietary staff
    C. Document the information in the patient's chart
    D. Ensure the information is passed on to the surgical team

Rationale:

Correct answer: D

Patients who are allergic to strawberries and avocados are at high risk for latex allergy, which the surgical team should be informed of. The surgical area can be made latex-free as a precaution to prevent an allergic reaction. Patients with allergies to bananas, kiwis, chestnuts, and passionfruit are also at higher risk for latex allergies.

A is incorrect because NPO status is important for a pre-operative patient but unrelated to allergy history or potential latex allergy.

B is incorrect because dietary staff can be notified at a later time. This is not a priority at this time, because the patient will be NPO prior to surgery.

C is incorrect because preventative care is a higher priority than documentation. It is the nurse's responsibility to be sure the pertinent information is passed on to the surgical team before the procedure is initiated to reduce the likelihood of a latex allergic reaction.

15. The nurse working in the allergy clinic is caring for clients. Which task below takes priority?

    A. Checking emergency equipment every morning
    B. Ensuring consent is obtained when needed
    C. Providing educational materials in several languages
    D. Teaching clients about managing their allergies

Rationale:

Correct answer: A

Safety is always priority in patient care. Emergency equipment should be checked every morning and medications available, so this is the priority action.

B is incorrect because informed consent is ultimately the healthcare provider's responsibility. The nurse acts as a witness, but obtaining consent is not the nurse's greatest priority.

C is incorrect because educational materials are important, but not the greatest priority. This addressed the patient's psychosocial needs, but safety is the biggest concern.

D is incorrect because teaching regarding allergies is important for the general patient population but not as much as a safety priority as answer choice.

16. The clinic nurse receives a call from a patient who has been exposed to poison ivy. The patient reports an itchy rash that has not been relieved by over-the-counter antihistamines. What is the best response by the nurse?

    A. "Antihistamines will not relieve poison ivy."
    B. "There are several antihistamines to try."
    C. "You need to come to the clinic right away."
    D. "You may need IV steroid treatment."

Rationale:

Correct answer: A

Poison ivy rash is caused by an allergic reaction to an oily resin found in the leaves, stems, and roots of poison ivy, poison oak, and poison sumac. The rash can be very itchy and last for weeks but generally goes away on its own. Antihistamines do not relieve poison ivy because this is a type IV reaction, and histamine is not a mediator of this type of reaction. The patient will need to be educated regarding this.

B is incorrect because antihistamines do not provide relief from poison ivy.

C is incorrect because the patient does not need to go to the clinic right away. The patient should be taught about the use of soothing lotions and cool baths to relieve the itching associated with poison ivy rash. Only if blisters or signs of a bacterial skin infection appear should the patient come see the healthcare provider.

D is incorrect because steroids may not be needed unless blisters appear or the rash persists for longer than 2-3 weeks. If steroids are indicated (commonly prednisone), the PO or topical route would be used ahead of IV steroids.

17. Plasmapheresis is ordered by the healthcare provider for a client with Goodpasture's syndrome. As the nurse is planning his care, which potential problem is the nurse's greatest priority?

    A. Reduced physical activity due to disease effects on the lungs
    B. Inadequate family coping related to patient's hospitalization
    C. Inadequate knowledge related to plasmapheresis process
    D. Potential for infection related to plasmapheresis

Rationale:

Correct answer: D

Goodpasture's syndrome is an uncommon autoimmune disease that affects both the kidneys and the lungs. Symptoms include fatigue, weakness, and loss of appetite caused by the body's antibodies attacking the lining of the lungs and the kidneys. This can lead to blood in the sputum or glomerulonephritis. Plasmapheresis may be performed to filter the blood and remove harmful antibodies. This treatment requires close hemodynamic monitoring and increases the patient's risk for infection.

A is incorrect because reduced activity will only be indicated if the vital signs and oxygenation status reflect the need. Risk for infection is a greater priority.

B is incorrect because family coping is not priority.

C is incorrect because inadequate knowledge is a definite potential but not as much of a priority as risk for infection.

18. The nurse has administered four doses of IV antihistamines to a patient experiencing severe allergy symptoms. What is the most important action by the nurse?

    A. Assess the patient's bedside glucose

B. Instruct patient not to get up without help

C. Monitor frequently for tachycardia

D. Record the intake, output, and weight

Rationale:

Correct answer: B

Drowsiness frequently occurs with the use of antihistamines, so the patient should call for help before getting up to prevent injury. Common side effects of antihistamines include drowsiness and dry mouth. More serious adverse reactions that the nurse should monitor for include sedation, bronchospasm, depression, and nightmares.

A is incorrect because blood glucose changes are not related to antihistamine administration.

C is incorrect because tachycardia is not a common adverse reaction to antihistamine treatment.

D is incorrect because intake, output, and weight are generally required for all patients but not directly related to antihistamine administration.

19. A patient on the medical floor has been receiving IV antibiotics for septicemia. When the nurse responds to their call light, the patient appears to have a swollen face and lips. What is the first action the nurse should take?

    A. Administer epinephrine 1:1000, 0.3 mg IV push immediately

    B. Apply a pulse oximeter and 100% oxygen by facemask

    C. Ensure a patent airway while calling the rapid response ream

    D. Reassure the patient that she will receive the best care

Rationale:

Correct answer: C

Anaphylaxis is a severe, multi-system response to an antigen-antibody reaction upon subsequent exposure to a substance for which the patient has developed a sensitivity. Large amounts of histamine are rapidly dispersed throughout the circulatory system causing extensive vasodilation and severe edema of bronchial tissues. This can lead to pulmonary obstruction. Especially when the face and lips become swollen, airway assessment is priority in the patient who has an allergic reaction to a medication. The nurse must assess patency of the airway and the rapid response ream should be notified for immediate assistance at the bedside. Other assessments the nurse might find include hypotension, tachycardia, dilated pupils, diaphoresis, dyspnea, and flushing.

A is incorrect because epinephrine may be needed, but the nurse must first determine if the airway is affected by the allergic reaction. Checking the airway is the first action the nurse should take.

B is incorrect because oxygen may be needed, but assessing the airway is priority. If the airway is swollen shut and the patient is not effectively breathing, applying high flow oxygen by mask will not help.

D is incorrect because reassurance is appropriate, but this meets the patient's psychosocial need. Airway is the physical priority.

20. A patient who is receiving treatment for a snake bite is suspected by the nurse of having serum sickness. Which lab result would be most concerning to the nurse?

    A. Blood urea nitrogen: 13 mg/dL
    B. Creatinine: 3.3 mg/dL
    C. Hemoglobin: 8.3 mg/dL
    D. White blood cell count: 13,000/mm3

Rationale:

Correct answer: B

Serum sickness is a type III hypersensitivity delayed immune response to either a medication (most commonly penicillin) or an anti-serum (such as is given for a snake bite). Symptoms include redness and itching at the injection site, hives, joint pain, fever, malaise, swollen lymph nodes, wheezing, and flushing. Antihistamines, NSAIDs, and corticosteroids are used to treat serum sickness. If untreated, serum sickness nephritis can occur, which manifests with elevated creatinine level. (Normal creatinine for an adult is 0.7-1.4 mg/dl; normal for a child is 0.4-1.2 mg/dl.)

A is incorrect because this blood urea nitrogen is normal (10-20 mg/dl). The nurse would expect to see elevated BUN if serum sickness nephritis is present.

C is incorrect because low hemoglobin is unrelated to serum sickness. (Normal for a male is 13-18 g/dl; normal for a female is 12-16 g/dl; normal for a child aged 3-12 is 11-12.5 g/dl.)

D is incorrect because the white blood cell count is slightly elevated but is not a sign of a complication with serum sickness.

21. A nurse working on the medical floor is assessing patients. Which action will prevent a type II hypersensitivity reaction in the clients?

    A. Steroid administration for severe serum sickness
    B. Correctly identifying patients prior to blood transfusions
    C. Keeping the patient free of offending agents
    D. Providing a latex-free environment for patients

Rationale:

Correct answer: B

A blood transfusion reaction is a type II hypersensitivity reaction. Correct identification of patients and cross-matching blood to be administered can prevent this type of reaction.

A is incorrect because serum sickness is a type III reaction.

C is incorrect because avoidance therapy is important for type I and IV hypersensitivities. Examples include allergic contact dermatitis (from poison ivy) and inflammatory bowel disease.

D is incorrect because latex allergy is a type I hypersensitivity: an allergic reaction provoked by exposure to a specific type of antigen called an "allergen." Other examples include allergic asthma, allergic rhinitis (hay fever), food allergies, and antibiotic allergies.

22. The nurse administers rivaroxaban to a patient. When the patient asks how the medication works, what is the best response by the nurse?

    A. "It inhibits thrombin."
    B. "It inhibits fibrinogen."
    C. "It keeps your blood from becoming too thin."
    D. "It works against vitamin K."

Rationale:

Correct answer: A

Direct thrombin inhibitors, like rivaroxaban, work by inhibiting the enzyme *thrombin*, which is instrumental in the formation of blood clots. Rivaroxaban interrupts the intrinsic and extrinsic blood clotting cascade, decreasing the likelihood of blood clot formation. The most serious adverse effect is bleeding.

B is incorrect because rivaroxaban does not affect fibrinogen. Heparin is an example of a drug that helps to prevent conversion of fibrinogen to fibrin. Another drug, pentoxifylline, is a hemorrheologic agent that reduces blood viscosity (used to treat peripheral arterial disease) and can decrease fibrinogen concentration in the blood.

C is incorrect because rivaroxaban causes the blood to become thinner and helps prevent clot formation.

D is incorrect because rivaroxaban does not work against vitamin K. Vitamin K is important in the blood clotting process, and it is used is the antidote to warfarin.

23. A patient on the medical-surgical unit is confused and mumbling, and upon reviewing the lab results, the nurse finds the platelet count is 8,000/mm³. Which action by the nurse takes priority?

    A. Calling the rapid response team
    B. Obtaining a set of vital signs
    C. Instituting bleeding precautions
    D. Placing the patient on bedrest

Rationale:

Correct answer: A

Normal platelet (thrombocyte) count is 150,000-450,000/mm³. The patient with severe thrombocytopenia is at risk for spontaneous bleeding. Since the patient has a neurologic change as well, the rapid response team should be notified for immediate bedside assistance.

B is incorrect because vital signs are important but not priority.

C is incorrect because instituting bleeding precautions is important, but the greatest priority is to address the confusion and mumbled speech. These signs of neurological decline can indicate cerebral hemorrhage.

D is incorrect because placing the patient on bedrest is important for general safety but does not address the potential bleeding.

24. The nurse is preparing a blood transfusion to hang on a patient in the surgical unit. The patient is recovering from a lower laminectomy spinal surgery. Current vital signs are HR 88, BP 118/72, temperature 98.9°F (37.2°C), and RR 18. Which of the following actions by the nurse is most important?

    A. Documenting of the vital signs before beginning the blood infusion
    B. Placing the patient on NPO status
    C. Placing the patient in protective isolation
    D. Putting on gloves

Rationale:

Correct answer: D

Standard Precautions are important when handling blood products to prevent bloodborne illness. Clean gloves should be worn before preparing the blood product for administration.

A is incorrect because documentation is not more important than safety.

B is incorrect because NPO status is unnecessary for a patient receiving a blood transfusion.

C is incorrect because protective isolation is unnecessary for a patient receiving a blood transfusion. Protective isolation is only required if the patient has been determined to be immunocompromised and thus highly susceptible to become infected.

25. The nurse on the oncology unit has just received the hand-off report on four patients admitted with leukemia. Which patient should be seen by the nurse first?

    A. Patient who passed two bloody diarrhea stools in the past four hours
    B. Patient who received promethazine before chemotherapy, complains of dry mouth
    C. Patient whose respiratory rate increased from 16 to 22 bpm
    D. Patient who has a lesion on the lower left lateral malleolus

Rationale:

Correct answer: A

Bloody stools indicate this patient may be suffering from acute gastrointestinal tract bleeding. This can be caused by the intense chemotherapy, which is used to treat leukemia. This is a potential circulatory emergency, which must be addressed first.

B is incorrect because promethazine is an anti-emetic which commonly causes dry mouth, so this is not most concerning to the nurse. Other side effects include drowsiness, dizziness, constipation, and urinary retention.

C is incorrect because the increase in respiratory rate may indicate infection or anemia. This patient should be seen next by the nurse.

D is incorrect because the patient with integumentary issues, such as a skin lesion, is not higher priority than potential bleeding.

26. A patient admitted to the medical unit for deep vein thrombus has developed petechiae after treatment. The platelet count is 43,000/mm³. The nurse will review the medication administration record for which medication?

    A. Enoxaparin
    B. Salicylates
    C. Unfractionated heparin
    D. Warfarin

Rationale:

Correct answer: C

Normal platelet (thrombocyte) count is 150,000-450,000/mm³. The patient with severe thrombocytopenia is at risk for spontaneous bleeding. Petechiae are indicative of heparin-induced thrombocytopenia. This is a condition in which the platelets are destroyed by use of heparin, leading to decreased platelet count. Petechiae can also develop after administration of antineoplastic medications and glucocorticoids.

A is incorrect because enoxaparin is low molecular weight heparin, which is less likely to cause heparin-induced thrombocytopenia than unfractioned heparin.

B is incorrect because salicylates are not associated with heparin-induced thrombocytopenia. Salicylates, such as aspirin, can cause GI bleeding, heartburn, and nausea.

D is incorrect because warfarin is not associated with heparin-induced thrombocytopenia. Warfarin can cause hemorrhage, diarrhea, rash, and fever.

27. A patient admitted to the emergency room for sickle cell crisis is complaining of right lower extremity pain of 10 out of 10. Which of the following comfort measures should the nurse delegate to the unlicensed assistive personnel (UAP) for this patient?

   A. Apply ice packs to the legs
   B. Elevate the lower extremities on pillows
   C. Keep lower extremities warm with a blanket
   D. Place compression wraps on the lower extremities

Rationale:

Correct answer: C

Sickle cell crisis causes decreased peripheral blood flow to the extremities due to occlusion of small blood vessels with sickled red blood cells. This causes extreme pain due to tissue ischemia. The patient needs to have the lower extremities kept warm, which promotes vasodilation and increases perfusion. This task can be delegated to the UAP.

A is incorrect because cold temperatures cause vasoconstriction, which will further decrease the tissue perfusion.

B is incorrect because elevating the extremities decreases blood flow to the area and will not help improve circulation and perfusion to the affected extremity. Elevation is used to decrease edema.

D is incorrect because compression wraps are contraindicated in sickle cell crisis.

28. A patient on the medical unit is receiving a blood transfusion. The patient calls the nurse to report anxiety and lower back pain. After stopping the blood transfusion, changing the IV tubing, and hanging normal saline, which of the following nursing actions is the most important?

A. Documenting the reaction in the patient's chart

B. Double checking patient and blood product for identification

C. Placing patient on strict bedrest

D. Reviewing the chart for known allergies

Rationale:

Correct answer: B

This patient has signs and symptoms characteristic of a hemolytic transfusion reaction. This type of reaction can be caused by ABO or Rh blood type incompatibility. The nurse must double check patient identification and blood product identification for blood typing. Other symptoms to be alert for include nausea, chills, vomiting, hypotension, tachycardia, hematuria, and decreased urine output. Normal saline should be infused IV immediately after stopping the blood.

A is incorrect because direct patient care is more important than documentation. The nurse must first address the potential hemolytic reaction ahead of documenting.

C is incorrect because bed rest is not necessary for a hemolytic reaction. Supportive care for a hemolytic reaction includes oxygen, diphenhydramine, and airway management.

D is incorrect because history of allergies is unrelated to hemolytic transfusion reaction.

29. A patient on the oncology ward is placed on neutropenic precautions. The family calls the nurse to report the patient "is not acting like himself." What is the priority action by the nurse?

    A. Inquire about pain

    B. Assess for infection

    C. Delegate vital signs

    D. Review lab results from this morning

Rationale:

Correct answer: B

Neutropenic patients are at increased risk of infection and may not display the normal signs and symptoms related to infection. Neutropenic precautions are instituted to prevent infection. The nurse needs to assess the patient for any type of infection which may be manifesting as change in level of consciousness or mentation.

A is incorrect because pain assessment is not a component of neutropenic precautions and this action will not provide information related to potential infection.

C is incorrect because this patient is not exhibiting expected behavior. The family's report suggests a change in level of consciousness, which can indicate infection. Vitals need to be taken, but they should not be delegated for this patient.

D is incorrect because lab results may not provide necessary information. A neutropenic patient may have an infection without elevated WBCs.

30. A 22-year-old male patient on the oncology unit is beginning treatment for lymphoma. Which of the following topics is priority for the nurse to teach the patient?

   A. Genetic testing
   B. Infection prevention
   C. Sperm banking
   D. Treatment options

Rationale:

Correct answer: C

Lymphoma (cancer of lymphoid tissue) is treated with radiation, which can destroy sperm and sperm-producing abilities, especially if the irradiated areas are near the pelvis or lower abdomen. Because it is difficult to predict the exact impact of cancer treatment on fertility, sperm preservation prior to cancer treatment is important for fertility preservation. Sperm banking should be discussed with this patient for future planning. In some cases, vinca alkaloid antineoplastic medications may be used in the treatment of lymphoma; these medications are less gonadotoxic than radiation.

A is incorrect because genetic testing is important but not priority.

B is incorrect because infection prevention is generally important for a lymphoma patient but not specifically a priority at the *beginning* of lymphoma treatment. It is important that the patient be offered information about sperm banking before radiation therapy begins.

D is incorrect because discussion of treatment options is important but not the responsibility of the nurse. The oncologist is responsible for reviewing treatment options with the lymphoma patient.

31. The nursing student on the medical unit is caring for a patient with HIV infection. The student knows which of the following traits regarding HIV are correct? (Select all that apply.)

    A. CD4+ cells create new HIV virus cells
    B. Antibody production is strengthened in the early stages
    C. Macrophages do not work properly
    D. Leading causes of death include opportunistic infection and cancer
    E. Stage 1 HIV is not infectious to others

Rationale:

Correct answer: A, C, D

Once in the body, the HIV virus attaches to CD4 cells (a type of WBC) and then multiplies, making more copies of HIV. Macrophages are phagocytic WBCs whose action is severely limited in HIV patients. Opportunistic infections (such as *P. jiroveci* pneumonia, *C. albicans* stomatitis, *C. neoformans* meningitis, and cytomegalovirus) and a form of cancer called Kaposi's sarcoma can take advantage of the body's weakened immune system.

B is incorrect because HIV is characterized by a weakened immune system which continues to weaken over time as the disease progresses.

E is incorrect because HIV is infectious, regardless of stage.

32. The nurse is caring for a patient with AIDS on the medical-surgical unit. Which of the following are characteristic of AIDS? (Select all that apply.)

    A. CD+4 count less than 200/mm³ or 14%
    B. *Pneumocystis jiroveci* pneumonia infection
    C. Positive ELISA test for HIV
    D. HIV wasting syndrome
    E. Antiretroviral medications prescribed

Rationale:

Correct answer: A, B, D

The AIDS diagnosis is confirmed with positive HIV and CD4+ less than 200/mm³ or 14% or opportunistic infection including *Pneumocystis jiroveci* plus HIV wasting syndrome. (HIV wasting syndrome isn't a disease specifically but refers to an HIV patient who has lost 10% of their muscle mass.)

C is incorrect because a positive ELISA test is not a characteristic of AIDS. The ELISA test confirms HIV.

E is incorrect because prescribed antiretroviral medication is not necessarily a characteristic of AIDS. Two other retroviruses that are capable of causing human infection include human T-lymphotropic virus type 1 and 2 (HTLV-1 and HTLV-II). Both these retroviruses are also treated with antiretroviral medications.

33. The nurse is on a mission trip in an under-developed country to care for those infected with HIV. The nurse recognizes which of the following as barriers to preventing transmission of HIV perinatally? (Select all that apply.)

   A. Clean drinking water
   B. Cultural concerns about bottle-feeding
   C. Lack of antiretroviral medication availability
   D. Social stigma
   E. Knowledge deficit related to HIV transmission routes

Rationale:

Correct answer: B, C, D, E

HIV treatment is complex, and there are numerous barriers in third world countries. Breastfeeding is cheaper and more convenient than bottle-feeding. Especially in low-income populations, some women are reluctant to accept treatment for HIV because they know they will be encouraged to bottle-feed instead of breastfeeding. These cultural and financial concerns about bottle-feeding can impact a woman's willingness to be tested or accept HIV treatment. Lack of medication availability is another barrier. Social stigma is a barrier too. Some women are reluctant to be tested for HIV while pregnant because they live in areas where they are prone to be beaten if their diagnosis is revealed within their community. Lack of education about perinatal transmission is a barrier as well. Transmission can occur across the placenta during birth, by exposure to body fluids during birth, and through breastfeeding with HIV-contaminated breastmilk.

A is incorrect because although lack of access to clean drinking water poses a serious health threat in third world countries, this is not specifically a barrier to preventing transmission of HIV from infected mother to baby. HIV is not transmitted via contaminated water.

34. A patient with AIDS is in the clinic seeing the nurse about difficulty in eating due to oral thrush. Which actions can be delegated by the nurse to the unlicensed assistive personnel (UAP)? (Select all that apply.)

    A. Applying oral anesthetic before eating
    B. Assisting with oral care every two hours
    C. Offering cool drink sips frequently
    D. Providing alcohol-based mouthwash
    E. Providing a soft toothbrush

Rationale:

Correct answer: B, C, E

Oral thrush is a yeast infection of the mouth characterized by white exudate and inflammation in the mouth and back of the throat. This is most commonly caused by *Candida albicans* and is very uncomfortable. Inflammation and irritation of the oral cavity make it difficult to eat and drink without pain. It is within the scope of practice of the UAP to assist with oral care, offer fluids to drink, and remind the patient of activities and interventions previously taught by the nurse.

A is incorrect because it is not within the UAP's scope of practice to administer any medications.

D is incorrect because an alcohol-based mouthwash will be ineffective in treating oral thrush and will cause further irritation and discomfort inside the patient's mouth. Nystatin swish-and-swallow or clotrimazole oral solution can be administered by the nurse to treat thrush.

35. The student nurse is caring for a patient on the medical-surgical unit for splenectomy. The student learns the functions of the spleen include which of the following? (Select all that apply.)

    A. Breakdown of hemoglobin
    B. Destruction of red blood cells that are old or defective
    C. Production of vitamin K
    D. Storage of iron
    E. Storage of platelets

Rationale:

Correct answer: A, B, E

The spleen resembles a large lymph node and is located in the upper left portion of the abdominal cavity (behind stomach). Its main functions are the destruction of worn-out blood cells, breakdown of hemoglobin, removal of foreign bacteria, platelet storage, and storage and release of blood during hemorrhage. The spleen also functions in immunity as a site of B cell proliferation into plasma cells.

C is incorrect because vitamin K production occurs in the liver. Vitamin K is a necessary component in the production of four coagulation factors.

D is incorrect because iron is recycled in the spleen but stored in the liver.

36. The nurse in the clinic knows there are many medications that impact the immune system. Which of the following medications are included that have this effect? (Select all that apply.)

    A. Acetaminophen
    B. Amphotericin B
    C. Sertraline
    D. Metformin
    E. Atorvastatin

Rationale:

Correct answer: B, C, E

The hematologic or immune system is disrupted by numerous medications. Amphotericin B is a powerful antifungal medication which is generally reserved only for progressive, potential life-threatening fungal infections. This medication can cause hematological abnormalities affecting the immune system such as leukopenia and eosinophilia. Sertraline is a SSRI antidepressant that increases serum serotonin levels and also boosts the immune system, sometimes even to the point of auto-immune disease. Atorvastatin is a drug used to lower cholesterol and has also been shown to reduce organ transplant rejection, indicating that it suppresses the immune system.

A is incorrect because acetaminophen is an antipyretic and analgesic that can cause liver damage but does not directly affect the immune system. In fact, acetaminophen is a safe drug of choice prescribed to treat the pain associated with many autoimmune disorders.

D is incorrect because metformin is an oral hypoglycemic agent used to treat type II diabetes, which does not affect the immune system.

37. A 65-year-old patient asks the clinic nurse why the immune system in people his age is weaker than in youth. What are the best responses by the nurse? (Select all that apply.)

    A. "Your bone marrow produces less blood cells than when you were younger."
    B. "You have decreased levels of platelets circulating in the bloodstream."
    C. "You have decreased levels of proteins and plasma in the bloodstream."
    D. "Lymphocytes are more reactive to foreign antigens."
    E. "The function of the spleen decreases after age 60."

Rationale:

Correct answer: A, C

As adults age, the bone marrow starts to produce fewer blood cells and blood volume is decreased with less plasma proteins. With age, the body's ability to determine self from non-self-diminishes, and macrophage activity slows.

B is incorrect because platelet count is only affected minimally by age, and platelets do not play a large role in immune function. Platelets are functional in blood clotting, and the normal platelet count is 150,000-450,000/mm^3.

D is incorrect because lymphocytes are less reactive with age, making the body more susceptible to infection.

E is incorrect because spleen function is not directly affected by age. Decreased spleen function in the elderly is commonly linked so other underlying medical disorders or disease processes.

38. The nurse is caring for a patient admitted with sickle cell anemia and is teaching them about self-management and prevention of sickle cell crisis. Which of the following does the nurse teach the patient about managing their disease? (Select all that apply.)

    A. "Avoid dehydration."
    B. "Minimize exercise and stay within your home as much as possible to prevent infection."
    C. "Avoid extremely stressful situations."
    D. "Take your antimetabolite medication daily."
    E. "Avoid opioids for pain control, as they can cause central nervous system depression."

Rationale:

Correct answer: A, C, D

Sickle cell disease is abnormal formation of red blood cells into a sickle shape, which makes it difficult to absorb and transport oxygen through the bloodstream. This leads to difficulty breathing, pain, and end organ damage. Sickle cell crisis can be precipitated by several factors including dehydration, high levels of stress, exposure to high altitudes, and pregnancy. Antimetabolites, analgesics, antibiotics, and vaccines are routine component of treatment for sickle cell anemia.

B is incorrect because sickle cell anemia is a chronic disease and the patient should be taught to stay as active as possible. Extreme vigorous exercise should be avoided, but exacerbation of sickle cell disease is unlikely to occur with a moderate exercise regimen. Although sickle cell patients are at greater risk for infection, they do not need to remain homebound. The nurse should teach the patient to avoid large crowds, where infection is most likely to be transmitted, but to remain active and independent within their community.

E is incorrect because sickle cell disease *is* often managed with oral acetaminophen and hydrocodone, or morphine as a part of the patient's daily analgesic medication regime at home. Ineffective pain control for sickle cell patients has been shown to contribute to social isolation, depression, inactivity, and decreased adherence to the medication regimen.

39. The student nurse on the oncology floor is learning about risk factors related to leukemia. Which of the following are risk factors for leukemia? (Select all that apply.)

    A. Chemical exposure
    B. Genetically modified foods
    C. Ionizing radiation exposure
    D. Vaccinations
    E. Viral infections

Rationale:

Correct answer: A, C, E

Leukemia is neoplastic disease that affects the blood-forming tissues of the body, including the lymphatic system, spleen, bone marrow, and blood cells. The effect is uncontrolled destruction of leukocytes. Risk factors for development of leukemia include ionizing radiation exposure, certain viral infections, and chemical exposure. People can be exposed to chemicals such as benzene, pyridine, and aniline at work (plastic, lubricant, rubber, and dye manufacturing), in the general environment (gasoline fumes), and through the use of some consumer products.

B is incorrect because consumption of genetically modified organisms (GMOs) is not a known risk factor for leukemia. GMOs have, however, been linked to allergies, pesticide exposure, and antibiotic resistance.

D is incorrect because vaccinations are not a known risk factor for leukemia.

40. A patient is admitted to the oncology unit for Ann Arbor stage Ib Hodgkin's lymphoma. Which manifestations does the nurse assess the patient for? (Select all that apply.)

    A. Headaches
    B. Night sweats
    C. Persistent fever
    D. Urinary frequency
    E. Weight loss

Rationale:

Correct answer: B, C, E

"Ann Arbor staging" is the staging system for both Hodgkin's and Non-Hodgkin's lymphomas. The stage depends on the location of malignant tissue and the severity of the symptoms. Ann Arbor stage Ib Hodgkin's lymphoma is characterized by single lymph node or single lymph region location of the disease with constitutional symptoms present, such as night sweats, persistent fever, and weight loss.

A is incorrect because headaches are not related to Hodgkin's lymphoma.

D is incorrect because urinary frequency is not related to Hodgkin's lymphoma.

NCLEX-RN – MED-SURG: GASTROINTESTINAL – 40 QUESTIONS

1. Traditional gastrostomy has been scheduled for a patient, and preoperative teaching has been completed. The patient and family verbalize understanding. What is the best action by the nurse?

    A. Arrange a tour of the ICU
    B. Assess patient's psychosocial status
    C. Document the patient teaching and response
    D. Have the patient begin nutritional supplements

Rationale:

Correct answer: B

A percutaneous endoscopic gastrostomy (PEG) is a safe and effective way to provide food, liquids, and medications (when appropriate) directly into the stomach. The gastrostomy procedure is performed to create a new opening to the stomach through the abdominal wall, for a feeding tube. It is a long and difficult procedure, and afterwards, the patient's normal nutritional and eating habits will be changed. The pre-operative teaching can cause the patient to be anxious. Psychosocial status should be assessed by the nurse to help further prepare the patient and family for the procedure. Worries about feeding supplies, home setup, and care of the gastrostomy tube should be addressed pre-op, if possible. The nurse can consult with home care services or a nutritionist to help alleviate anxiety about the upcoming change in daily life.

A is incorrect because the patient should be offered a tour *after* psychosocial needs have been addressed. A tour may actually increase anxiety about the procedure, so the nurse should not offer this until after anxiety level has been determined.

C is incorrect because documentation should be performed after psychosocial issues have been assessed and addressed. Documentation never takes priority over patient care.

D is incorrect because nutritional supplements may be started before the procedure, but the nurse must first determine when the patient is going to the OR. The patient must be NPO prior to the start of the procedure.

2. A patient is admitted to the surgical unit following open Nissen fundoplication. An indwelling urinary catheter, two peripheral IVs, and nasogastric (NG) tube are in place. The nurse connects the NG tube to low intermittent wall suction. The nurse notes bright red blood in the suction canister from the NG tube. What is the first action the nurse should take?

   A. Document in the patient's chart
   B. Immediately notify the surgeon
   C. Measure the drainage, empty the canister, and reassess the drainage in one hour
   D. Obtain vital signs

Rationale:

Correct answer: D

A Nissen fundoplication is a laparoscopic procedure performed to treat hiatal hernia and gastroesophageal reflux disease (GERD). Drainage from the NG tube following the procedure should be brown, indicating normal GI contents or old blood. Bright red blood in the suction canister and NG tube indicates active bleeding, which is an abnormal finding. The nurse should obtain a full set of vital signs to identify signs of shock. Hypotension and tachycardia are indications of shock. Vitals should be reassessed frequently to determine if BP is dropping. The nurse should be prepared to increase the IV fluid rate.

A is incorrect because documentation should be completed after patient care has been completed. It is negligent to document before assessing and treating the symptom, which indicate a GI bleed.

B is incorrect because the surgeon should be notified immediately after vital signs are obtained. Vital signs are pieces of data that the nurse can collect quickly at the bedside, and this is information which the surgeon will want to know.

C is incorrect because obtaining vital signs should be the first action. Waiting an hour to re-assess is doing nothing for the current problem and could delay emergency treatment.

3. The nurse is caring for a patient on the medical-surgical unit who had a Zenker's diverticulum removed yesterday. The patient's NG tube, which is set to low intermittent suction, has had no drainage for the past four hours. The surgeon did not leave specific orders for the NG tube. What is the most appropriate action by the nurse?

   A. Reposition the patient for comfort and document the findings
   B. Irrigate NG tube with 20 mL normal saline
   C. Notify the surgeon
   D. Remove the NG tube and insert a new one

Rationale:

Correct answer: C

Zenker's diverticula (also known as "false diverticula") occur in the hypopharynx, usually in elderly patients, as the result of esophageal mucosa herniation. The result is an outpouching of the posterior pharyngeal wall, just above the esophagus, and can lead to dysphagia, regurgitation, and aspiration. The patient will be NPO postoperatively for several days, or until swallowing has been re-established. The surgically placed NG tube should be draining small amounts of gastric juice, green-to-brown in color with a low pH. The nurse should not advance, withdraw or manipulate the tube in any way. Irrigation should not be performed without specific direction from the healthcare provider. The surgeon needs to be notified about the absence of drainage.

A is incorrect because the absence of drainage is an abnormal finding which must be addressed ahead of documentation. Repositioning the patient may help facilitate drainage, but notifying the surgeon is the priority. The question does not state that the patient is in discomfort.

B is incorrect because surgically placed NG tubes should not be irrigated without an order from the surgeon.

D is incorrect because the patient needs temporary gastric decompression while healing from the surgery and removing the NG tube will require a new one to be placed, which can be traumatic to the patient. Surgically-placed NG tubes should not be removed without an order from the surgeon.

4. A patient in the emergency department has esophageal trauma. Subcutaneous emphysema with crepitus in the mediastinal area up to the lower part of the neck is palpated by the nurse. What is the priority action the nurse should take?

    A. Assess oxygenation status

    B. Order a STAT chest X-ray

    C. Prepare patient for surgery immediately

    D. Start a large-bore peripheral IV

Rationale:

Correct answer: A

Subcutaneous emphysema indicates air has leaked under the skin. This can occur from a ruptured esophagus. Airway is priority in this patient. Oxygenation status needs to be assessed by the nurse before any diagnostic procedure. Vomiting, chest pain, and subcutaneous emphysema are the "Macklers's triad" of symptoms that indicate esophageal perforation.

B is incorrect because before ordering a chest X-ray (and while awaiting the X-ray), the nurse is responsible for assessing the respiratory system and intervening if the patient is not oxygenating well.

C is incorrect because oxygenation status must be assessed first. If the patient's airway is not patent with equal breath sounds bilaterally, the nurse will perform emergency interventions before preparing for surgery.

D is incorrect because the patient needs IV access, but respiratory concerns take priority over fluid replacement in this patient who is demonstrating an airway issue.

5. When caring for a patient with a nasogastric (NG) tube, what action by the nursing student requires intervention by the registered nurse?

    A. Checking NG tube placement every four hours

    B. Monitoring NG tube drainage and documenting

C. Pinning the tube snug to the patient gown, with the head in the midline position

D. Providing oral care every four hours

Rationale:

Correct answer: C

The NG tube should be pinned to the patient gown, but the patient should be able to turn their head without pulling on the NG tube. Pinning the tube without enough slack will risk withdrawal of the tube when the patient changes position or turns their head from side-to-side.

A is incorrect because checking NG tube placement every four hours is appropriate. Checking placement can be done by measuring the tube and comparing to the previously documented measurement or by checking pH of NG tube contents.

B is incorrect because monitoring and documenting NG tube drainage is appropriate and these actions are within the scope of practice of a nursing student.

D is incorrect because providing oral care every four hours is appropriate for a patient with a NG tube in place.

6. A Nissen fundoplication with nasogastric (NG) tube placement was performed on a patient the previous day. During rounds, the nurse finds the patient vomiting bright red blood, and the NG tube is on the bed. What is the first action the nurse should take?

    A. Notify the surgeon
    B. Don gloves
    C. Reinsert NG tube
    D. Obtain vital signs

Rationale:

Correct answer: B

A Nissen fundoplication is a laparoscopic procedure performed to treat hiatal hernia and gastroesophageal reflux disease (GERD). The nurse must put on a pair of clean gloves first, to prevent exposure to the blood. The nurse should remain at the bedside, facilitate proper positioning to prevent aspiration of the vomit, and suction as necessary. Vital signs should be obtained and oxygen applied if necessary.

A is incorrect because notifying the surgeon is appropriate but not the first action. The nurse must stay with the patient and delegate to another member of the nursing team to notify the surgeon.

C is incorrect because a NG tube that was placed in surgery should not be replaced at the bedside by the nurse. Furthermore, the nurse does not insert an NG tube into a patient who is actively vomiting. The insertion could cause aspiration of the vomit, leading to further complications. The vomiting must be controlled before a new tube is inserted.

D is incorrect because obtaining vital signs is priority, but the nurse must be protected by wearing gloves before coming into contact with blood or any other bodily fluid.

7. A patient is admitted to the medical-surgical unit for peptic ulcer disease. The patient calls the nurse to report sharp abdominal pain that started suddenly. When the nurse palpates the abdomen, it is rigid and tense. What is the priority action by the nurse?

    A. Administer pain medication
    B. Notify the healthcare provider
    C. Percuss the abdominal quadrants
    D. Obtain vital signs

Rationale:

Correct answer: B

Peptic ulcer disease is manifested by erosion of the lining of the stomach and duodenum due to overproduction of hydrochloric acid. Other causes include excessive alcohol consumption, severe stress, NSAID and corticosteroid use, and *H. pylori* infection. This patient has several signs and symptoms of a perforated ulcer, which include severe epigastric pain spreading across the abdomen, with abdominal rigidity, hyperactive-diminished bowel sounds, and rebound tenderness. The healthcare provider must be notified immediately for medical attention.

A is incorrect because treatment of pain does not take priority over other actual physical problems. Oral medications, especially, should not be administered in case NPO status is required for surgery. Opiates should be withheld until the nurse determines if a surgical consent needs to be signed.

C is incorrect because further assessing the abdomen (percussion) is not priority at this time. The nurse has enough assessment to call the healthcare provider.

D is incorrect because vital signs will not initially give vital information about a perforated ulcer.

8. A patient is in the emergency department reporting pain from peptic ulcer disease that has worsened over the last few days. Blood pressure when supine was 122/80 mmHg and 98/52 mm Hg upon standing. What is the most appropriate action by the nurse?

    A. Administration of ibuprofen
    B. Notify the rapid response team
    C. Start an IV and administer normal saline
    D. Keep the patient on bedrest

Rationale:

Correct answer: C

The patient is displaying signs of dehydration or fluid volume loss with the orthostatic changes in blood pressure. The patient needs an IV and isotonic solution, or normal saline, to replace the fluid lost.

A is incorrect because NSAID medications, such as ibuprofen, should be avoided in a patient with peptic ulcer disease. Generally, H2-receptor antagonists and proton pump inhibitors can be administered to alleviate the pain associated with peptic ulcer disease.

B is incorrect because the rapid response team is not necessary for orthostatic hypotension. The nurse should first administer fluids and reassess to determine if the BP stabilizes in response to fluid replacement.

D is incorrect because the patient should be put on bedrest, but this nursing action does not address the fluid deficit or the blood pressure.

9. A patient is being taught by the nurse about medications for *Helicobacter pylori* infection. What is the most question for the nurse to ask?

A. "How much alcohol do you consume each week?"

B. "Do you have a family history of *H. pylori* infection?"

C. "Do you use nicotine patches?"

D. "Do you think you will be able to take several medications daily?"

Rationale:

Correct answer: D

H. pylori infection is treated with a combination of several drugs, so it can be difficult to adhere to the drug therapy. The nurse needs to assess the patient's ability and willingness to adhere to the treatment program. Drugs to treat *H. pylori* include metronidazole (usually used along with another antibiotic), an H2-receptor antagonist such as cimetidine (blocks acid production), and bismuth subsalicylate, which coats the ulcer and protects from stomach acid.

A is incorrect because although alcohol can worsen peptic ulcer disease, alcohol consumption is not directly related to teaching the patient about medications.

B is incorrect because personal or family history of *H. pylori* infection history is not more important than determining compliance with treatment regimen. This information is also unrelated to teaching about medications.

C is incorrect because although nicotine and tobacco smoke can increase gastric acid production, this is not the most important thing to address.

10. Esomeprazole has been prescribed for chronic gastric ulcers in a 55-year-old female patient. What is particularly important for the nurse to teach this patient?

A. Ask the pharmacist about taking other medications

B. Increase calcium and vitamin D intake

C. Notify healthcare provider of worsening symptoms

D. Medication must be taken each morning

Rationale:

Correct answer: B

Chronic gastric ulcers are commonly caused by overproduction of gastric acid, which is improved with the use of a proton-pump inhibitor (PPI) such as esomeprazole. Long term use of this medication has been shown to lead to osteoporosis and fractures, so the patient should be taught to increase calcium and vitamin D intake at the start of the medication therapy.

A is incorrect because esomeprazole does not commonly interact with other medications.

C is incorrect because notifying the healthcare provider of worsening symptoms is generally appropriate but not specific to esomeprazole.

D is incorrect because esomeprazole is taken at night to prevent nocturnal acid production.

11. The nurse responds to a patient's call light and finds them in the bathroom. The patient has vomited a large amount of bright red blood. After applying gloves, what is the first action the nurse should take?

    A. Assist patient back to the bed
    B. Immediately notify the healthcare provider
    C. Measure the bloody vomit
    D. Obtain vital signs

Rationale:

Correct answer: A

After donning gloves to protect the nurse from exposure to the blood, the priority action is to safely assist the patient back to bed, where the nurse can further assess them.

B is incorrect because notifying the healthcare provider is appropriate, but this can be delegated to another member of the nursing team. The patient who has vomited blood is unstable, and the nurse should stay with the patient.

C is incorrect because assisting the patient to bed is a safety measure that takes priority. After the patient has been assessed and appropriate nursing interventions have been performed, the vomit can be measured, documented, and cleaned up. Furthermore, this action can be delegated to a UAP.

D is incorrect because if the patient is internally bleeding, he may be hypotensive and light-headed and at risk for a fall. Obtaining vital signs is appropriate after the patient is safely back in bed.

12. The nurse cares for a patient with upper gastrointestinal hemorrhage and a nasogastric (NG) tube in place. The blood pressure has been dropping, and a 1 liter bolus of 0.9% NS requires comfort measures. Which comfort measure may be delegated to the unlicensed assistive personnel (UAP) by the nurse?

   A. Lavage NG tube with cold water
   B. Frequent oral care
   C. Reposition NG tube every four hours
   D. Obtaining frequent vital signs

Rationale:

Correct answer: B

Oral care is important to perform for the patient with an NG tube for comfort and infection prevention. This is a standard task that can be delegated to the UAP. In order for a task to be delegated to the UAP, it must frequently recur in the daily care of patients, be performed according to an established sequence of steps, and involve little or no modification from one patient situation to another. Tasks that are performed with a predictable outcome and do not inherently involve ongoing assessment, interpretation, or decision-making, and do not endanger a patient's life or well-being, are able to be delegated to the UAP.

A is incorrect because lavage of the NG tube is not within the scope of practice of a UAP. Lavage is performed by the nurse because it requires judgment about type and amount of fluid used, amount of force to use when injecting the fluid, and evaluating for patient response.

C is incorrect because repositioning of the NG tube is not typically required and is not within the scope of practice of a UAP. If needed, repositioning requires consultation with the healthcare provider and will be performed by the nurse.

D is incorrect because vital signs can be delegated to the UAP, but this is not a comfort measure.

13. The nurse is caring for a female patient diagnosed with gastric cancer. Before sending the patient to the preoperative area for a total gastrectomy procedure, which of the following lab values would the nurse report to the surgeon immediately?

A. Albumin 2.3 g/dL

B. Hematocrit 31%

C. Hemoglobin 9.2 mg/dL

D. International normalized ratio (INR) 4.3

Rationale:

Correct answer: D

INR is a measure of bleeding time and is routinely checked for patients taking warfarin. Normal INR is 1.0. This patient's level is elevated, which indicates bleeding risk. The surgeon should be notified of this result immediately because of the increased risk for bleeding during the procedure. The patient may need vitamin K supplementation or the procedure postponed until the INR is normalized.

A is incorrect because a decreased albumin level is expected with gastric cancer. Protein digestion begins in the stomach and continues in the small intestine, so in patients with gastric cancer it is common to have decreased protein levels. Normal serum albumin is 3.5-5.5 g/dL.

B and C are incorrect because these are expected findings in a patient with stomach cancer. Ulcers and cancers of the esophagus, stomach or intestines are some of the most serious causes of chronic gastrointestinal blood loss, leading to decreased hemoglobin and hematocrit. Normal hemoglobin for a male is 13-18 g/dl, normal for a female is 12-16 g/dl, normal for a child aged 3-12 is 11-12.5 g/dl. Hematocrit measures percentage of red blood cells per fluid volume of blood. Normal hematocrit is 42-52% for men, 35-47% for women, and 35-45% for children.

14. The clinic nurse cares for a male, 63-year-old patient with a history of type II diabetes, stomach cancer, and hypercholesterolemia. He has just been informed that his stomach cancer has returned and he is very upset. Vitals are BP 125/74, pulse 88, RR 14, and SpO$_2$ 97%. What is the most appropriate response by the nurse?

    A. "Who do you have for support?"

    B. "Tell me what you're feeling."

    C. "We knew this might happen."

    D. "Would you like a referral to hospice?"

Rationale:

Correct answer: B

The patient's vital signs are normal, so the nurse should focus on how upset the patient is. Asking the patient about his feelings is therapeutic and demonstrates willingness to listen to concerns. This is an open-ended question which will facilitate the nurse-patient relationship and help determine the patient's emotional state. Once rapport is established, the nurse can then help the patient to understand treatment options and offer reassurance, as appropriate. (The history of diabetes and hypercholesterolemia are unrelated to the current situation.)

A is incorrect because the nurse should first help the patient identify his feelings related to his diagnosis. Open-ended communication about how the patient is currently feeling focuses on the patient and will help the nurse help the patient. Asking about others who can support the patient can be done after establishing rapport.

C is incorrect because this nursing response dismisses the patient's feelings.

D is incorrect because it is a yes/no question, which is non-therapeutic. The patient may not need hospice care yet.

15. The nurse is caring for a 71-year-old female patient who is recovering from a partial gastrectomy due to stomach cancer. The patient has had six loose stools in the past 12 hours. Which action by the nurse is best, initially, for this patient?

    A. Dietary consult arrangement
    B. Encourage the patient to drink 8 oz of fluid with three meals daily
    C. Offer tea and coffee between meals to replenish fluid lost from diarrhea
    D. Encourage the patient to lie down after meals

Rationale:

Correct answer: D

Dumping syndrome commonly occurs after surgery to the stomach that causes foods to move from the stomach, through the small intestine, and through the colon rapidly, causing frequent diarrhea. Nutrients are not properly absorbed, as the contents of the GI tract are moved through too quickly. This can lead to malnutrition and dehydration. Other symptoms such as fatigue, sweating, fainting, mental confusion, and tachycardia may be present. Gravity facilitates movement through the GI system, so lying down after meals can slow this process and promote more absorption. Other instructions include avoiding sugary foods and limiting fiber.

A is incorrect because the nurse should implement specific nursing interventions ahead of consulting another service.

B is incorrect because the patient experiencing dumping syndrome should be encouraged to eat six small meals daily. PO fluids should not be consumed with meals because fluids increase speed of movement through the GI system. The patient should consume fluids between meals to meet daily fluid needs to prevent dehydration.

C is incorrect because caffeine is a stimulant which speeds movement through the GI tract. Caffeine should be avoided in a patient with dumping syndrome.

16. A 78-year-old female client is scheduled for partial gastrectomy for cancer. The family requests the patient not be informed of the diagnosis. What is the best action by the nurse?

    A. Ask family why they feel the patient shouldn't be informed
    B. Assess the family's concerns and fears
    C. Refuse to follow family's wishes
    D. Inform the family the patient must be notified of her diagnosis.

Rationale:

Correct answer: B

The nurse must assess the family's concerns and fears using open-ended questions for therapeutic communication. The Self-determination Act is a federal law requiring health care facilities to provide written information to adult patients about their rights to make health care decisions. Generally, the patient has a right to know their diagnosis and the plan of treatment.

A is incorrect because "why" questions are not therapeutic. Asking "why?" leads people to feel they need to defend themselves. The nurse should ask open-ended questions that encourage discussion, without the use of the word "why?"

C is incorrect because refusing to follow family's wishes does not help foster the nurse's relationship with the family and does not promote trust.

D is incorrect because telling the patient against their wishes will not help the nurse's relationship with the family. If the patient is alert and oriented, and able to understand spoken language, she will have the legal right to know her diagnosis, but it is better, first, to further address the family's concerns in a therapeutic way. The nurse must determine if the family feels the patient is psychologically unstable or at risk of harming herself. It is also important for the nurse to determine of the family has durable power of attorney or guardianship if the patient is mentally incapacitated.

17. The nurse is teaching a patient with a new diagnosis of irritable bowel syndrome (IBS) about dietary choices. Which of the following menu selections demonstrates the patient understands the instructions?

    A. Ham on white bread, applesauce, diet ginger ale
    B. Baked chicken, brown rice, steamed cauliflower, apple juice
    C. Grilled cheese, banana, hot tea
    D. Baked tilapia, green beans, coffee with milk

Rationale:

Correct answer: B

Irritable bowel syndrome (IBS) is a gastrointestinal (GI) disorder that causes a cluster of symptoms in adults and children including abdominal pain, bloating, cramping, diarrhea, gas, and altered bowel habits (constipation, diarrhea, or both). This is a functional disorder; the problem is related to motility, not damage to the actual organs of the GI system. Patients with this diagnosis should consume high levels of fiber (30-40 g per day) and plenty of fluids. Soda should be avoided, and the patient should consume smaller meals. The menu choice with the highest amount of fiber is baked chicken, brown rice, cauliflower, and apple juice (brown rice and cauliflower contain high amounts of fiber).

A is incorrect because only the applesauce is high fiber. Ham on white bread does not have a high amount of fiber, and soda should be avoided with IBS. Artificial sweeteners, as contained in diet soda, and high-fructose corn syrup, which is often found in regular soda, can both irritate the bowel of a patient with IBS.

C is incorrect because only the banana has high fiber. The grilled cheese sandwich menu selection should specify "on whole wheat bread" for added fiber.

D is incorrect because tilapia and green beans do not have a high amount of fiber. Caffeinated beverages, such as coffee, and milk products can cause worsened symptom in IBS.

18. A female patient with a history of severe irritable bowel syndrome (IBS) comes to the clinic. She has been taking alosetron, as prescribed, since her last visit, six weeks ago. She reports feeling depressed and anxious about her bowel habits. What is an important question the nurse should ask the patient?

   A. "Have you had any constipation?"
   B. "Have you been getting enough fiber and fluids?"
   C. "Would you like to talk to the healthcare provider about an order for fluvoxamine?"
   D. "Have you experienced hypertension?"

Rationale:

Correct answer: A

Alosetron is indicated only for women with severe diarrhea-predominant irritable bowel syndrome (IBS) who have not responded to conventional treatment. A side effect is constipation, which can lead to complications such as ischemic colitis and mesenteric ischemia (both are life-threatening). The patient should be assessed for any constipation and if present, the health care provider should be notified, and the medication should be withheld.

B is incorrect because fiber and fluid intake are beneficial for someone with severe IBS, but determining if the patient has experienced any constipation is most important with alosetron.

C is incorrect because fluvoxamine (SSRI) is contraindicated with alosetron and this medication should not be ordered for the patient.

D is incorrect because alosetron does not cause or treat hypertension, so this is an irrelevant assessment.

19. The nurse is caring for a male, 49-year-old patient with a femoral hernia and a history of type II diabetes. The patient is not a candidate for hernia repair surgery. The nurse teaches

the patient about the use of a truss pad. Which patient statement demonstrates more teaching is needed?

    A. "I will put the truss on when I go to bed every night."

    B. "I will put on powder under the truss to prevent skin irritation."

    C. "Because I am unable to have surgical repair, the truss will help the hernia."

    D. "I will notify the healthcare provider of abdominal pain."

Rationale:

Correct answer: A

A truss is a support garment that holds the intestine in place to lessen protrusion of a hernia. The truss should be put on before getting out of bed in the morning and worn throughout the day. The patient's statement indicated poor understanding of the need to wear the truss during the day.

B is incorrect because powder *can* be used under the truss, indicating correct understanding.

C is incorrect because the truss *is* used in place of surgery, indicating correct understanding.

D is incorrect because the healthcare provider *should* be notified of abdominal pain, indicating correct understanding.

20. The nurse cares for a male 68-year-old patient who is post op day 1 from hemorrhoidectomy. The nurse assesses the patient at shift change and notes lower abdominal distension that is dull to percussion. Which action should be taken by the nurse?

    A. Assess vital signs

    B. Determine last urinary void by the patient

    C. Ask if the patient has passed gas since the surgery

    D. Auscultate the abdomen

Rationale:

Correct answer: B

Lower abdominal distension that is dull to percussion is indicative of a full bladder. Urinary retention is common postoperatively, so the nurse must determine the last time the patient

133

voided. The patient should be encouraged to void, and if unable, straight catheterization may be needed.

A is incorrect because vital signs will not give significant information related to bladder fullness or urinary retention.

C is incorrect because presence of flatus is not related to bladder function. Assessment of flatus (and bowel sounds) is necessary to determine of the patient is ready to have his diet advanced.

D is incorrect because auscultation of the abdomen is not the most important action. The correct sequence for abdominal assessment is inspection and auscultation, followed by palpation and then percussion (IAPP). The auscultation should have been completed before the nurse percussed the abdomen.

21. A nurse at the community health center is assessing clients. Which client is at highest risk for developing colorectal cancer?

   A. 35-year-old female who drink five cups of coffee per day, exercises six times per week, and has a history of melanoma
   B. 45-year-old male with irritable bowel syndrome, eats five servings of vegetables daily, consumes one glass of red wine daily
   C. 64-year-old Asian American male who works 60 hours/week
   D. 64-year-old Native American female who frequently eats fast food

Rationale:

Correct answer: D

This patient has two risk factors: age over 50 and diet.

Modifiable risk factors for colorectal (colon) cancer include being overweight (or obese), smoking, physical inactivity, diet high in red meat or processed meats, low-fiber/high-fat diet, and heavy alcohol use. Non-modifiable risk factors include personal history of type II diabetes, colorectal polyps, colorectal cancer, or inflammatory bowel disease (Crohn's disease or ulcerative colitis). Age over 50 and family history of colorectal cancer are also risk factors. Racial and ethnic background also affects one's risk: African Americans have the highest colorectal cancer incidence and mortality rates of all racial groups in the United

States. Jews of Eastern European descent (Ashkenazi Jews) have one of the highest colorectal cancer risks of any ethnic group in the world.

A is incorrect because this patient has no risk factors. Neither coffee intake nor caffeine increases colorectal cancer risk. Regular physical exercise actually *reduces* the risk for colon cancer. Melanoma does not increase one's risk for colorectal cancer.

B is incorrect because this patient has no significant risk factors for colorectal cancer.

C is incorrect because this patient has one risk factor: age over 50. Working overtime does not increase colorectal cancer risk. Asian Americans are not at higher risk than other ethnic groups.

22. The nurse is assessing a 59-year-old male patient admitted to the surgical unit with colorectal cancer. The patient has a history of urinary tract infections. The nurse notes high-pitched bowel sounds and visible peristaltic waves when inspecting the patient's abdomen. Which of the following actions should be taken by the nurse?

   A. Ask the patient if he is experiencing any right shoulder pain
   B. Assess the patient's rectum for polyps
   C. Contact the healthcare provider and request a computed tomography scan
   D. Administer a laxative to increase movement of the bowel

Rationale:

Correct answer: C

High-pitched bowel sounds and visible peristaltic waves indicate partial obstruction of the bowel which can be a result of colorectal cancer. The healthcare provider should be contacted so computed tomography can be performed to diagnose the obstruction.

A is incorrect because right shoulder pain (referred pain) is associated with peritonitis and cholecystitis. Referred pain in the upper thorax muscles is seen in patients with inflammation of organs in the abdominal cavity.

B is incorrect because an internal rectal examination to assess for polyps is not within the scope of practice of the registered nurse.

D is incorrect because laxatives are not indicated until after the obstruction has been verified and the healthcare provider determines whether or not surgery is needed.

23. The nurse cares for patients on the medical unit. The 61-year-old, male patient, who has just been informed of his diagnosis of colon cancer, says to the nurse, "Please tell my visitors that I don't want any company today." Which action should the nurse take?

    A. Contact the healthcare provider and request a psychiatric consult
    B. Ask the patient about feelings related to the new colon cancer diagnosis
    C. Provide education regarding treatment options
    D. Encourage friends and family to visit and provide support

Rationale:

Correct answer: B

A new diagnosis of cancer of any type can be detrimental to a patient. Initially, the patient may experience denial and depression related to the diagnosis. The patient should be encouraged to verbalize these feelings so the nurse can assist with moving through the grief stages. Note: Kubler-Ross's stages of grief are as follows: denial, anger, bargaining, depression, and acceptance. However, not all patients experience these stages in this particular order.

A is incorrect because psychiatric consult may be needed, but the nurse should focus on the patient in the here and now, first. The nurse should always attempt to do *something* for the patient, ahead of "passing-the-buck" to another member of the professional team.

C is incorrect because discussion of the patient's feelings should occur *before* treatment options are presented. The healthcare provider (not the nurse) is responsible for offering treatment options. Furthermore, providing education before the patient is ready avoids discussing the patient's feelings.

D is incorrect because the nurse should focus on the patient's concerns. Inviting visitors to see the patient, against the patient's wishes, may cause the patient to lose trust in the nurse. The patient has already stated that no visitors are wanted. It is more important to focus on the nurse-patient communication at this time.

24. A patient with colon cancer has recently had a colostomy placed. The patient says, "I would like to speak with someone with a similar experience. I think it would help me." What is the best response by the nurse?

A. "My neighbor has a colostomy and would probably be willing."

B. "The enterostomal therapist should be able to answer your questions."

C. "I can refer you to the United Ostomy Associations of America."

D. "Most people who have colostomies don't talk about them because it is such a private matter."

Rationale:

Correct answer: C

Nurses can better help patients if they know about community-based resources. The United Ostomy Associations of America (ostomy.org) has local chapters with resources. Arrangements can be made to have visitors who have experienced similar surgical procedures for ostomy placement talk to the patient.

A is incorrect because the nurse should not use a personal contact to speak with a patient. It is important for the nurse to keep professional and personal life separate.

B is incorrect because the enterostomal therapist may be an expert in stoma care, but the patient is asking to speak to someone with a colostomy. The nurse should meet the patient's needs by connecting the patient with someone who has had a similar medical experience.

D is incorrect because the statement dismisses the patient's concern.

25. The nurse is caring for a patient in the emergency room after a motor vehicle accident. When performing the initial physical assessment, the nurse notes bruising across the lower abdomen. Which is the first action the nurse should take?

A. Measure abdominal girth

B. Assess abdomen for guarding or rigidity

C. Check the most recent lab results for hemoglobin and hematocrit

D. Assess complete health history

Rationale:

Correct answer: B

After a traumatic injury, bruising on the abdomen accompanied by guarding or rigidity may indicate major internal organ injury and the patient may be bleeding internally. Determining whether the patient has these additional symptoms is imperative.

A is incorrect because measuring abdominal girth is not necessary at this time. Internal hemorrhage may be present before the nurse notes increase in abdominal girth measurement.

C is incorrect because assessing lab results is not the first action. Initial labs drawn upon arrival to the emergency department may not indicate slow bleeding from trauma to visceral organs. Immediate physical assessment of the patient takes priority.

D is incorrect because taking a complete health history is a general assessment which should be completed but is not the *first* action the nurse should take. The nurse should remain focused on the here-and-now situation.

26. A nurse is caring for a 38-year-old female patient who had a colostomy placed three months ago. The client says her husband refuses to be intimate with her because of the colostomy. What is the best response by the nurse?

    A. "Shall we talk, together, with your husband about his concerns related to intimacy and your colostomy?"
    B. "Longer lingerie can be worn to hide the appliance."
    C. "You can empty the pouch more frequently, so your husband won't notice it as much."
    D. "Sexual activity can cause stoma harm, if you're not careful."

Rationale:

Correct answer: A

A colostomy is a new opening made in the large intestine through the abdominal wall where stool will pass into a pouch or appliance. The nurse should try to facilitate open communication between the patient and the spouse about sexual concerns with the colostomy. Collaboration with the ostomy nurse can also help the patient and spouse work through issues related to intimacy after colostomy.

B is incorrect because suggesting longer lingerie is dismissive of the patient's concerns. (The nurse should not assume that the patient wears lingerie.)

C is incorrect because although more frequent emptying of the pouch can help eliminate odor, this doesn't enable open communication about the colostomy's effect on sexual behavior.

D is incorrect because sexual activity does not cause stoma harm. Many colostomy patients are able to return to normal sexual activity with the collection bag in place.

27. The patient recovering from hemorrhoidectomy tells the nurse he feels the need to have a bowel movement. Which of the following actions should be taken by the nurse?

    A. Assign a UAP to place a bedside commode in the room
    B. Provide for privacy, but stay with the patient
    C. Place the call light in reach, so the patient can call when finished
    D. Obtain a specimen container for stool sample

Rationale:

Correct answer: B

Hemorrhoidectomy is a surgical removal of hemorrhoids, internal or external. After the surgical procedure, the first bowel movement can be extremely painful and can even cause syncope. The nurse should assist the patient to the bedside commode or bathroom and stay with the patient for the bowel movement.

A is incorrect because a bedside commode may be necessary, but it is more important that the patient not be left alone.

C is incorrect because the call light should be within reach, but this does not meet safety needs.

D is incorrect because a stool sample is not necessary. Stool sample is indicated for a patient who needs laboratory testing to assess for bacterial infection, such as *C. difficile*, or parasites. The patient after a hemorrhoidectomy is not necessarily at risk for these complications unless other symptoms are present.

28. The nurse in the emergency department cares for a patient who experienced a gunshot to the abdomen. The patient's BP is 88/62, pulse is 126 bpm, and RR is 26. Which action should the emergency room nurse take first?

    A. Send blood for type and cross-matching
    B. Start a large IV for fluid replacement
    C. Obtain vital signs
    D. Assess and maintain airway

Rationale:

Correct answer: D

The vital signs (low BP, high pulse, high RR) suggest hemorrhage. Airway is the nurse's priority, especially in a patient who has sustained trauma.

A is incorrect because type and cross-matching blood is an appropriate nursing action, but the airway needs to be assessed first. Intubation will take place before supplemental blood products are hung.

B is incorrect because IV and fluids are appropriate, but not the first action that should be taken. Establishing an airway is the nurse's primary concern.

C is incorrect because vital signs is an appropriate nursing assessment but not the first needed action.

29. A male patient in the emergency room, with a diagnosis of mechanical bowel obstruction, is experiencing intermittent abdominal pain. Later, the patient reports constant abdominal pain. What is the next action the nurse should take?

    A. Administer opioid medications, as ordered, intravenously
    B. Position the patient's knees to his chest
    C. Insert NG tube attached to low-wall suction for gastric decompression
    D. Assess bowel sounds

Rationale:

Correct answer: D

Due to the change in abdominal pain the patient is experiencing, the nurse must assess bowel sounds and check for rebound tenderness, which can be due to peritonitis or bowel perforation.

A is incorrect because pain medications should not be administered until the nurse further assesses the change.

B is incorrect because repositioning the patient may lessen or alleviate the abdominal pain, but determining the cause of the pain is the greater priority.

C is incorrect because an NG tube is invasive and may not be needed. The nurse should implement least-invasive measures first.

30. A client is receiving intravenous 5-fluorouracil chemotherapy for colon cancer. Which finding would cause the nurse to contact the healthcare provider?

    A. WBC 1400/mm³
    B. Fatigue
    C. Nausea and diarrhea
    D. Oral ulcers and mucositis

Rationale:

Correct answer: A

5-fluorouracil is an antineoplastic medication used for chemotherapy. Side effects include fatigue, nausea, diarrhea, oral ulcers, bone marrow depression, liver dysfunction, and mucositis. This patient's WBC count is extremely low, placing the patient at high risk for infection, so the healthcare provider should be notified.

B is incorrect because fatigue is a common side effect of fluorouracil.

C is incorrect because nausea and diarrhea are common side effects of fluorouracil.

D is incorrect because oral ulcers and mucositis are common side effects of fluorouracil.

31. The nurse cares for a 46-year-old male patient who had an ascending colon colostomy placed two weeks ago. The client states the stool in the pouch is still liquid. What is the best response by the nurse?

    A. "This type of colostomy will always have liquid stool."
    B. "If you eat more fiber, this will bulk up the stool."
    C. "The stool will be firmer over time."
    D. "I will contact the healthcare provider because this is not normal."

Rationale:

Correct answer: A

A colostomy placed in the ascending colon will always have liquid stool output because fluid is reabsorbed in the distal portions of the large intestine. The patient's statement indicates the need for further instruction about expected outcomes after an ascending colon colostomy placement.

B is incorrect because fiber will not bulk up the stool at this location.

C is incorrect because the stool will not firm up over time.

D is incorrect because this is a normal finding for a patient with an ascending colostomy placement.

32. A 50-year-old male client with irritable bowel syndrome (IBS) has made changes to his diet and taken bulk-forming laxatives but states his symptoms have not improved. He asks the nurse if lubiprostone treatment might help his symptoms. What is the best response by the nurse?

    A. "The drug is still being researched and is not available yet."

    B. "Lubiprostone is only approved for female patients, but we can talk about other treatment options."

    C. "Lubiprostone is an effective drug; I will recommend it to the healthcare provider."

    D. "Bulk-forming laxatives should not be used with lubiprostone."

Rationale:

Correct answer: B

Lubiprostone is a drug given for chronic constipation associated with irritable bowel syndrome (IBS). It works by stimulating intestinal receptors for increased fluid absorption and increased bowel transit time. It is only approved for use in women. The nurse should respond therapeutically, by giving factual information and suggesting other options for this patient.

A is incorrect because lubiprostone was approved by the FDA in 2006 and has since been used in female patients.

C is incorrect because lubiprostone is not yet approved for use in male patients.

D is incorrect because lubiprostone can be used safely with bulk-forming laxatives in women.

33. The nurse is providing education for a male patient who is recovering from colon resection. Which of the following statements does the nurse include in the plan of care?

    A. "Nausea and vomiting may be experienced for a few weeks."

B. "Acid reflux can be decreased with moderate consumption of carbonated beverages."

C. "Stool softeners will make it easier to have a bowel movement."

D. "Your normal workout routine may be resumed, as long as you take it easy."

Rationale:

Correct answer: C

Colon resection is performed to remove part of the large intestine to prevent or remove diseases and conditions affecting the colon. Stool softeners can be taken to make bowel movements easier after colon resection surgery.

A is incorrect because nausea and vomiting should not be expected. These symptoms could indicate obstruction or perforation of the intestines and must be reported to the healthcare provider immediately.

B is incorrect because carbonated beverages should be avoided after colon resection surgery because they can be irritating to the GI system.

D is incorrect because exercise and weight lifting should be completely avoided after colon resection surgery. The patient may be instructed to resume normal physical activities after the first post-op clinic visit.

34. The nurse is caring for a patient who is at risk for colon cancer. Which dietary recommendation should the nurse include when teaching the patient?

   A. "Consume low-fiber, low-residual foods."
   B. "It's easier to digest white bread and rice."
   C. "Cauliflower and broccoli should be added to your diet."
   D. "Animal fat foods will protect the mucosa of the intestines."

Rationale:

Correct answer: C

A patient who is at risk for colon cancer should increase intake of high-fiber foods, including cauliflower and broccoli, while decreasing animal fats and refined carbohydrates. Other sources of fiber may include whole grain products, beans, peas, and nuts.

A is incorrect because a low-fiber diet increases the risk for colon cancer. A high fiber-diet will help prevent colon cancer.

B is incorrect because foods rich in simple carbohydrates, such as rice and white bread, are not high in fiber. A high-fiber diet will help prevent colon cancer.

D is incorrect because animal fat foods do not protect the mucosa of the intestines.

35. A patient with a new colostomy is being cared for by the nurse. Which of the following actions should be taken by the nurse?

   A. Empty the colostomy pouch frequently to remove collections of excess gas
   B. Change the pouch and wafer of the ostomy every morning
   C. Allow complete filling of the pouch before emptying
   D. Apply surgical tape to secure pouch and prevent any leakage

Rationale:

Correct answer: A

A new ostomy pouch should be emptied frequently (when the pouch is 1/3 to 1/2 full), due to excess gas production after placement.

B is incorrect because the pouch and wafer do not necessarily need to be changed daily.

C is incorrect because the pouch should be emptied when 1/3 to 1/2 full.

D is incorrect because surgical tape should not be used on ostomies because of the risk for skin breakdown.

36. A 35-year-old male patient arrives at the clinic. He has a family history of colon cancer. His father and brother had cancer, and he wants to know what the chances are that he will be diagnosed with colon cancer. What is the best response by the nurse?

   A. "Eating a low-fat, low-fiber diet will decrease your chances significantly."
   B. "Colon cancer is autosomal dominant and skips generations, so you will be safe."
   C. "Preventive surgery plus chemotherapy can remove the cancer cells and prevent the disease."
   D. "You should have colonoscopies more often for early identification of abnormal polyps."

Rationale:

Correct answer: D.

Modifiable risk factors for colorectal (colon) cancer include low-fiber/high-fat diet. Frequent colonoscopies should be encouraged for early identification of abnormal/cancerous cells.

A is incorrect because a low-fat, *high*-fiber diet decreases chances of developing colon cancer.

B is incorrect because colon cancer does *not* skip generations. Family history of colon cancer increases this patient's risk.

C is incorrect because preventive surgery and chemotherapy can decrease risk but do not prevent cancer, ultimately.

37. A 64-year-old patient in the emergency room has been admitted for *Salmonella* poisoning. The patient's heart rate is 104 bpm, blood pressure 96/56 mmHg, respirations 24 bpm, and oxygen saturation 97%. What is the first action the nurse should complete?

    A. Apply oxygen
    B. Administer IV fluids
    C. Provide perineal care
    D. Teach proper food preparation

Rationale:

Correct answer: B

Older patients who experience *Salmonella* poisoning can develop dehydration from vomiting and diarrhea quickly. This patient's vital signs suggest the patient is hypotensive and tachycardic, with elevated respirations, in response to dehydration. Restoring fluid balance is important in this population. Prompt administration of IV fluids is the priority nursing action.

A is incorrect because additional oxygen is not necessary for a patient with an oxygen saturation of 97%.

C is incorrect because caring for the perineum is a standard component of care but does not directly address the dehydration.

D is incorrect because teaching proper food preparation is appropriate before the patient is discharged home but not the first action.

38. A client with viral gastroenteritis is receiving dietary instruction from the nurse. Which instruction should be included in the client's teaching?

    A. "Drink extra fluids for prevention of dehydration."

    B. "Limit your fluids to 1 liter per day."

    C. "Drink milk to increase protein intake."

    D. "Nausea can be relieved with small sips of tea or cola."

Rationale:

Correct answer: A

In viral gastroenteritis (more commonly referred to as the stomach flu), the lining of the stomach, small intestine, and large intestine become inflamed, causing vomiting and/or diarrhea. This can be caused by several different viruses and is highly contagious and extremely common. The most common complication is dehydration. Fluids should be encouraged to replace water lost in the vomit and diarrhea.

B is incorrect because fluids should not be limited in viral gastroenteritis. A normal adult needs at least 2 liters of fluid daily, so suggesting the patient limit fluids to 1 liter is not appropriate to meet hydration needs.

C is incorrect because milk products are not recommended with viral gastroenteritis as they can further irritate the GI tract and worsen diarrhea.

D is incorrect because caffeine increases motility of the intestinal tract and can worsen diarrhea. Carbonated beverages, such as ginger ale or lemon-lime soda, may be tolerated with viral gastroenteritis; however, the high fructose corn syrup used to sweeten most sodas can also be irritating.

39. A 55-year-old male patient hospitalized with *Salmonella* food poisoning has been educated by the nurse. Which statement made by the patient indicates additional teaching is needed?

    A. "I will have my wife do all the cooking."

    B. "The ciprofloxacin should be taken until diarrhea resolves."

    C. "I will wash my hands with antibacterial soap before eating."

    D. "Dishes should be placed in the dishwasher after eating."

Rationale:

Correct answer: B

Salmonella gastroenteritis infection is generally not treated with antibiotics unless the infection becomes systemic. In that case, ciprofloxacin (a fluoroquinolone antibiotic) is the drug of choice. This medication is taken for 10 days to two weeks. The medication should be taken until completed, even after the diarrhea or other symptoms subside.

A is incorrect because people who have *Salmonella* should not prepare foods because this is highly contagious and can be transferred person-to-person. The patient's statement indicates correct understanding.

C is incorrect because hands should be washed with antibacterial soap before eating, indicating correct understanding. The nurse should also teach the patient about the importance of proper handwashing after using the bathroom, because *Salmonella* can be transferred via the fecal-oral route.

D is incorrect because the statement indicates the patient understands that the dishwasher is the preferred method of cleaning dishes to eradicate *Salmonella* bacteria. (Handwashing dishes is not recommended when a member of the household has *Salmonella* poisoning.) Dishes, silverware, and cups should not be shared.

40. Which clinical symptoms should the nurse expect to find in a patient experiencing exacerbation of Crohn's disease?

    A. Positive Murphy's sign, rebound tenderness
    B. Dull, hypoactive bowel sounds heard in bilateral lower abdominal quadrants
    C. High-pitched rushing sounds in the right lower quadrant
    D. Abdominal cramping that worsens at night

Rationale:

Correct answer: C

Crohn's disease is inflammatory bowel disease that causes abdominal pain, fatigue, severe diarrhea, malnutrition, and weight loss. Crohn's disease causes narrowing of the bowel lumen, (often in the ileum and the ascending colon, in the right lower abdominal quadrant) and thus would cause the nurse to hear high-pitched rushing sounds.

A is incorrect because Murphy's sign is not used with Crohn's disease. Murphy's sign refers pain during inspiration while the examiner's fingers are pressing on the location of the gallbladder. A positive Murphy's sign indicates cholecystitis; a negative Murphy's sign is seen with choledocholithiasis (bile duct stones), pyelonephritis (kidney infection), and cholangitis (bile duct infection). Rebound tenderness is used to determine peritonitis.

B is incorrect because Crohn's disease is not characterized by dullness or hypoactive bowel sounds.

D is incorrect because Crohn's disease is not characterized by worsening abdominal cramping at night. Abdominal pain in patients with Crohn's disease is usually worse after meals.

NCLEX-RN – MED-SURG: RENAL – 40 QUESTIONS

1. The nurse is assessing patients on the medical unit. The nurse identifies which of the following patients at highest risk of developing bacterial cystitis?

    A. 35-year-old female who is nulliparous

    B. 45-year-old male taking cyclophosphamide

    C. 60-year-old female who has declined hormone replacement therapy

    D. 75-year-old male admitted with mild congestive heart failure

Rationale:

Correct answer: C

Bacterial cystitis is inflammation of the bladder as a result of bacterial infection. It most commonly occurs in women and sometimes children. Post-menopausal women who are not taking estrogen replacement are at highest risk for bacterial cystitis due to urethral and vaginal changes of cells. Recent urinary catheterization is another risk factor for cystitis. Symptoms include burning on urination, cloudy urine, and a strong odor to the urine. Treatment includes antibiotics, urinary tract analgesics (phenazopyridine), and saw palmetto herbal supplement. Cranberry juice or other urine acidifiers may be beneficial as well.

A is incorrect because the nulliparous female is not as at risk as the older woman not taking hormones.

B is incorrect because men are not susceptible to bacterial cystitis due to the longer urethra. Cyclophosphamide is an alkylating antineoplastic agent used to treat leukemia and multiple myeloma. Adverse effects include bone marrow suppression, ototoxicity, and renal toxicity, but not cystitis.

D is incorrect because men are not as susceptible as women due to the longer urethra, and CHF is not a risk factor for cystitis.

2. The nurse is reviewing lab results of a patient who has a urinary tract infection. The nurse notes a shift to the left in the white blood cell count. Which of the following actions should be taken by the nurse?

   A. Call the lab for differential analysis of white blood cells
   B. Notify the healthcare provider for parenteral antibiotics
   C. Instruct the unlicensed assistive personnel (UAP) to strain the patient's urine for calculi
   D. Assess for allergic reaction or anaphylactic shock

Rationale:

Correct answer: B

A shift to the left in white blood cells indicates an increase in the number of bands and is suggestive of urosepsis. This is not seen in urinary tract infection with no complications. The nurse needs to notify the healthcare provider and prepare for administration of IV antibiotics.

A is incorrect because a shift to the left is determined by reading the differential analysis of white blood cells. This is a blood test that has already been completed, so it does not need to be repeated.

C is incorrect because shift to the left does not indicate kidney stones, so straining the urine for calculi is not necessary. Symptoms of kidney stones include flank pain radiating to the shoulder, diaphoresis, nausea, vomiting, hematuria, and WBCs and bacteria in urine.

D is incorrect because shift to left indicates infection, not allergic reaction. Increased eosinophil count would cause the nurse to be concerned about allergy or anaphylaxis. Signs of anaphylaxis include hypotension, dyspnea, decreased oxygenation, and flushing.

3. A 68-year-old female is in the family clinic after a second episode of bacterial urethritis in six months. When the patient asks the nurse why this is happening now, as she never had urinary tract infections before, what is the best response by the nurse?

A. "The immune system doesn't weaken with age, so we will need to look into this further."

B. "Decreased estrogen levels increase tissue susceptibility to infection."

C. "You must be more diligent about personal hygiene in that area."

D. "You may have a sexually transmitted disease that has been left untreated."

Rationale:

Correct answer: B

Bacterial urethritis is inflammation of the urethra due to bacterial infection. Decreased estrogen levels decrease normal levels of moist secretions in the perineal area. This, along with tissue changes, predispose the area to infections. Postmenopausal women commonly develop urethritis due to these changes.

A is incorrect because the immune system does weaken with age. However, the more likely cause for this patient's infection is decreased estrogen levels.

C is incorrect because personal hygiene does not often contribute to bacterial urethritis risk.

D is incorrect because sexually transmitted disease may cause urethritis, however due to this patient's age, the infection is most likely due to decreased estrogen levels.

4. The nurse in the clinic is caring for a patient who has been experiencing overflow incontinence. In order to assist the patient with elimination, which intervention does the nurse include?

A. Medial aspect of the thigh is stroked

B. Intermittent catheterization

C. Digital anal stimulation

D. Valsalva maneuver

Rationale:

Correct answer: D.

Overflow incontinence is due to involuntary urine release from the bladder when it is overfull, yet the patient lacks the urge to urinate. This leads to urine leaking during the day and bed-wetting at night. The voiding reflex arc is absent, causing incontinence. Valsalva maneuver, or bearing down, and holding the breath (similar to while defecating), provides mechanical pressure that can assist in initiating voiding of urine.

A is incorrect because stroking the thigh will not stimulate urination when the reflex arc is not intact.

B is incorrect because intermittent catheterization increases the risk of infection and is only implemented when all other interventions are unsuccessful. The nurse should attempt non-invasive interventions first.

C is incorrect because digital anal stimulation will not work to elicit urine output when the reflex arc is not intact.

5. The nurse on the medical unit is caring for a patient admitted for pneumonia who has an indwelling urinary catheter. The day after admission, the nurse should ask the healthcare provider which of the following questions during interdisciplinary rounds?

    A. "Would you like daily weights?"
    B. "Is the patient able to be discharged home?"
    C. "Can the indwelling urinary catheter be discontinued?"
    D. "Would you like a chest X-ray today?"

Rationale:

Correct answer: C

Urinary tract infections (UTIs) are the most common type of healthcare-associated infection, and 80% of these are caused by indwelling urinary catheters, which can also lead to urosepsis. These catheters should only be left in as long as medically necessary, yet many catheters are often used or continued without valid medical indication. The nurse should advocate for the patient by consulting with the healthcare provider daily regarding continuing medical need for catheterization and possible discontinuation of the catheter. After catheter removal, the nurse must assess the patient for voiding every two hours for six to eight hours. If the patient is unable to void after six to eight hours or complains of discomfort or voids more than 250 mL over two to four hours, the nurse should consider assessing bladder volume with bladder ultrasound.

A is incorrect because daily weights are appropriate but not priority in this patient and not related to the catheter.

B is incorrect because discharge home is appropriate to ask about but not priority in this patient and not related to the catheter.

D is incorrect because a chest X-ray is appropriate but not priority in this patient and not related to the catheter.

6. The nurse is teaching a patient regarding renal calculi. Which patient statement demonstrates correct understanding?

    A. "I need to increase my fluid intake to 2 liters per day."
    B. "All dairy and calcium sources should be eliminated from my diet."
    C. "Aspirin and products that contain aspirin can lead to stones."
    D. "I will notify the healthcare provider for antibiotics when I experience signs of a stone."

Rationale:

Correct answer: A

Renal calculi, or kidney stones, are deposits of minerals that form in the kidneys, usually due to dehydration. Renal calculi lead to obstruction and urinary stasis. The patient needs adequate fluid intake in order to prevent dehydration and likelihood of stone formation. It is important not to over-hydrate (increases pain) or under-hydrate (increases length of time to pass stone). Other causes of renal calculi may include hypercalcemia, immobility, and gout.

B is incorrect because although hypercalcemia may cause kidney stones, all calcium does not need to be eliminated from the diet. Adequate calcium is required for skeletal structure support, adequate nerve impulse transmission, muscle contraction, absorption, blood clotting, and enzyme activation. The patient should also be taught about limiting intake of oxalates, which can lead to stone formation (oxalates are found in swiss chard, peanuts, wheat germ, cola, tea, chocolate, and spinach.)

C is incorrect because aspirin and products that contain aspirin do not lead to stone formation. Aspirin can increase risk for bleeding and should not be administered to patients younger than age 21. Medications that can lead to stone formation include: topiramate (anticonvulsant), anti-gout medications, and calcium supplements. Hyperparathyroidism also can lead to stones.

D is incorrect because antibiotics do not treat or prevent stone formation. Analgesics will be encouraged or provided when a patient is experiencing kidney stones, and antibiotics will only be necessary if the stone leads to signs of infection (fever, foul-smelling urine, pus in urine.)

7. A patient on the medical-surgical floor has just had extracorporeal shock wave lithotripsy to treat renal calculi. When assessing the patient, the nurse notes ecchymosis to the right side of the lower back. Which of the following actions should be taken by the nurse?

    A. Prepare to administer fresh frozen plasma
    B. Apply ice to the site
    C. Have the patient lie in prone position
    D. Draw labs for serum coagulation levels

Rationale:

Correct answer: B

Extracorporeal shock wave lithotripsy is the use of high energy sound waves through the skin to break down kidney stones into smaller pieces that are able to pass through the ureters to be eliminated through the urethra. The shock waves may cause bleeding in the tissues it passes through, so ecchymosis is a common finding that does not require high level intervention. Applying ice to the site can reduce blood flow to the area, decreasing bruising and discomfort.

A is incorrect because fresh frozen plasma (FFP) is not indicated for lithotripsy or bruising. FFP is used for reversal of anticoagulant effects.

C is incorrect because prone position will not have an effect on bruising.

D is incorrect because serum coagulation tests are not indicated. The patient has not been given any medications that affect coagulation, and lithotripsy does not affect coagulation either. The bruising is an expected finding and should be monitored.

8. The nurse on the medical unit is caring for four patients. Which patient does the nurse identify as being at greatest risk for bladder cancer?

    A. 27-year-old female who has had venereal diseases
    B. 45-year-old male who has spent 10 years working in a lumber yard

C. 50-year-old female who has frequent bacterial cystitis

D. 84-year-old male who has a 40-pack year history of smoking

Rationale:

Correct answer: D

Bladder cancer is most frequently found in older adults (age over 55), and if found early, treatment is often successful. However, bladder cancer can often recur, so patients must follow up with their health care provider routinely. Modifiable risk factors for bladder cancer include smoking, not drinking enough fluids, and arsenic in drinking water (uncommon in the U.S.). Non-modifiable risk factors include history of chronic infections of the urinary tract, race (Caucasian people are twice as likely to get bladder cancer than other races), age, and gender (men are more likely to get bladder cancer than women).

A is incorrect because venereal diseases do not increase risk of bladder cancer. Patients who have had prior chemotherapy or radiation or who have family members who have had bladder cancer are at greater risk.

B is incorrect because working in a lumber yard does not increase risk of bladder cancer. Certain occupations (painters, machinists, printers, hairdressers, and truck drivers) are at higher risk for cancer, due to exposure to toxins.

C is incorrect because frequent bacterial cystitis is one risk factor, but patient D has three risk factors (age, gender, smoking).

9. The nurse in the surgical unit is caring for a patient who had a complete cystectomy and ileal conduit placement. For which of the following assessment findings would the nurse identify as a need to contact the healthcare provider immediately?

    A. Ileostomy drains blood-tinged urine

    B. Presence of sero-sanguineous drainage on surgical dressing, mucous surrounding stoma

    C. Pale and bluish color noted on stoma assessment

    D. Oxygen saturation 93%

Rationale:

Correct answer: C

Complete cystectomy is removal of the bladder. Ileal conduit placement involves removal of a small portion of the small intestine to be used to facilitate drainage of urine from the ureters through a small opening in the abdomen, called a stoma. The stoma empties urine into an external urostomy bag. The stoma should always be soft, moist, and pink-to-red in color. The stoma should not be painful to touch, as it has no nerve endings. Pale and cyanotic tissue, including an ileostomy stoma, is an indication of impaired circulation. The healthcare provider needs to be notified to intervene and prevent tissue necrosis.

A is incorrect because blood-tinged urine is an expected finding after complete cystectomy and ileal conduit placement.

B is incorrect because sero-sanguineous drainage and a small amount of mucous are expected findings after complete cystectomy and ileal conduit placement. Bright red drainage would be an indication of hemorrhage, and foul-smelling drainage would be indication of infection; both of these findings would be reason to call the healthcare provider.

D is incorrect because the oxygen saturation level is slightly low (normal is 95% or above), but the nurse can encourage coughing and deep breathing and reposition the patient to facilitate better oxygenation before calling the healthcare provider.

10. A patient with suspected bladder cancer is in the clinic with the nurse. When documenting health history, which of the following questions does the nurse ask to determine risk factors?

    A. "Are you a cigarette smoker?"
    B. "Do you drink alcohol?"
    C. "Do you currently use any recreational drugs?"
    D. "What prescription medications are you taking?"

Rationale:

Correct answer: A

Bladder cancer is most frequently found in adults over the age of 55. Smoking is the single greatest modifiable risk factor for preventing development of bladder cancer.

B is incorrect because drinking alcohol does not increase risk of bladder cancer.

C is incorrect because use of recreational drugs is not linked to increased risk of bladder cancer. However, marijuana use has been found to increase the risk for testicular cancer.

D is incorrect because rarely do prescription drugs increase risk of bladder cancer. The exceptions are medications containing phenacetin (which has been banned in the U.S. since 1983) and long-term use of cyclophosphamide.

11. The nurse is performing preoperative care for a patient scheduled for surgical ileal conduit creation. When the patient tells the nurse he is anxious about the procedure and wants to know what the drainage tube will be like, what is the best response by the nurse?

    A. "I can notify the healthcare provider for antianxiety medication."

    B. "Would you like me to call the healthcare provider to talk to you about the procedure again?"

    C. "It would be convenient to not have to look for a bathroom."

    D. "Would you feel better if you could talk with someone who has undergone the procedure?"

Rationale:

Correct answer: D

Positive self-image is an important goal for a patient who will have an ileal conduit placed. It is important for the nurse to provide information to help relieve the patient's anxiety. Arranging for a conversation between the patient and someone who has had the same procedure done can help provide information. Other appropriate nursing interventions include showing the patient a picture of the drainage tube, reading through an informational pamphlet with the patient, and using words to describe the tube and the post-operative goals for the patient regarding urine elimination.

A is incorrect because asking for antianxiety medication does not answer the patient's question and does not promote positive self-image. The nurse should always attempt to reduce anxiety with non-pharmacologic measures first.

B is incorrect because having the healthcare provider explain the procedure again does not promote positive self-image. The nurse should focus on providing information to the patient and calling the healthcare provider is not needed. The nurse is capable of providing information.

C is incorrect because sharing an opinion does not answer the patient's question; this is a dismissive statement and does not promote positive self-image. Whenever the patient asks a question, it is important to select the answer that addresses the question.

12. The nurse is teaching a 19-year-old female about amoxicillin, which has been prescribed for a urinary tract infection. Which of the following statements should be included by the nurse?

    A. "Use two forms of birth control while taking the amoxicillin."
    B. "Increased menstrual bleeding is common while taking amoxicillin."
    C. "An irregular heartbeat is common while taking amoxicillin."
    D. "Watch your urine for blood while taking amoxicillin."

Rationale:

Correct answer: A

Amoxicillin is in the drug class of penicillin medications, which are bactericidal. They are used to treat UTIs by inhibiting cell-wall synthesis in susceptible gram-positive organisms. Penicillin drugs have been known to reduce effectiveness of contraceptives that contain estrogen, so a second form should be used while taking amoxicillin. Patients should also be taught to take this medication one hour before or two hours after meals, to reduce gastric acid destruction of the medication. It is also important for the nurse to teach the patient to take the full course of the medication, even after symptoms resolve.

B is incorrect because amoxicillin does not cause increased menstrual bleeding. Adverse effects of penicillin medications include glossitis, superinfections, diarrhea, and gastritis.

C is incorrect because an irregular heartbeat is not expected when taking amoxicillin.

D is incorrect because blood in the urine is not an expected finding with amoxicillin. If the patient's UTI caused blood in the urine, the amoxicillin should help resolve the issue. If the blood in the urine persists, the patient should call the healthcare provider.

13. A patient experiencing functional urinary incontinence is being taught by the nurse in the clinic. Which of the following statements does the nurse include?

    A. "Clean daily around the catheter with soap and water."

B. "Vaginal weights must be washed with 10% bleach solution after use."

C. "You can consider operations for bladder repair."

D. "Slacks with elastic waistbands are recommended for easy removal."

Rationale:

Correct answer: D

Functional urinary incontinence is inability to get to the bathroom for physical or mental reasons that results in leakages of urine, in either small or large volume. Independent management of clothing is a reasonable goal for these patients. The nurse should instruct the patient to select loose-fitting clothing with stretch waist bands rather than buttons or zippers. Buttons, snaps, and multilayered clothing should be avoided, and substituting Velcro for hooks and zippers can be beneficial. Elastic waistbands provide for easier removal when the patient gets to the bathroom. Functional urinary incontinence can be related to cognitive disorders (delirium, dementias), neuromuscular limitations impairing mobility, impaired vision, weakened pelvic muscles, and environmental barriers.

A is incorrect because patients with functional urinary incontinence do not necessarily have a catheter in place.

B is incorrect because vaginal weights are not cleaned with bleach. If using vaginal weights to strengthen pelvic floor muscles (which can help with incontinence), soap and warm water should be used before and after each use of the weights.

C is incorrect because functional urinary incontinence is not treated with bladder repair surgical procedures.

14. A patient with urinary incontinence is in the clinic experiencing an extremely dry mouth, acute constipation, and is unable to void. Which of the following questions does the nurse ask the patient first?

    A. "Have you been drinking enough water?"

    B. "What are your current medications?"

    C. "Have you recently used a laxative or enema?"

    D. "Have you experienced this before?"

Rationale:

Correct answer: B

Urinary incontinence is inability to control the flow of urine and results in small to large leakages of urine. Incontinence can be treated with anticholinergic agents including propantheline, with side effects that can include dry mouth, acute constipation, and retention of urine. The medication list needs to be assessed by the nurse to see if an anticholinergic medication is being taken by the patient.

A is incorrect because although the patient's symptoms are indicative of dehydration, asking about medications is more important to help the nurse identify the cause of these symptoms.

C is incorrect because recent use of a laxative or enema would not cause the symptoms listed and is not related to this situation.

D is incorrect because asking about previous experiences is not helpful for this situation. Focusing on the patient here-and-now is more important than assessing history.

15. The nurse in the recovery room is caring for a patient recovering from urologic procedure. Which of the following assessments would alert the nurse to a possible urine flow obstruction?

    A. Severe pain
    B. Slowed urine stream
    C. Hypotension
    D. Blood-tinged urine

Rationale:

Correct answer: B

Urologic procedures sometimes result in urethral stricture, and a common manifestation of this is urine flow obstruction. Slowed urine stream, sometimes described as a "dribble," is a sign of obstruction. Other manifestations of obstruction include patient complaint that the bladder does not feel empty after voiding, decreased urine output, or distended bladder.

A is incorrect because severe pain is not characteristic of urine flow obstruction. Some post-op pain is expected, and should be treated with analgesics, but severe pain should be investigated by the nurse.

C is incorrect because hypotension is concerning and can be indicative of fluid volume depletion or post-op shock but is not characteristic of urine flow obstruction.

D is incorrect because blood-tinged urine is common and expected after a urologic surgical procedure and is not characteristic of urine flow obstruction.

16. A patient tells the nurse they are embarrassed by their urinary incontinence and it feels like they have a child's bladder. What is the best response by the nurse?

    A. "I understand. I would be embarrassed, too."
    B. "If you wear incontinence pads, it will minimize public leaks."
    C. "There are strategies for controlling incontinence you can learn."
    D. "It happens to more women than you think."

Rationale:

Correct answer: C

Urinary incontinence is inability to control the flow of urine and results in small to large leakages of urine. This strategy demonstrates the nurse acknowledging the patient's concerns. The patient can be taught strategies to control the incontinence which would be helpful to the patient.

A is incorrect because although it is reflective, this is not the best way to address the patient's concerns. It's important to respond in a manner that focuses on the patient, not the nurse. "I" statements are nurse-focused.

B is incorrect because it minimizes the patient's concerns. It would be more helpful to teach the patient strategies for strengthening pelvic floor muscles and planning bathroom trips than to simply wear incontinence pads.

D is incorrect because it does not address the patient's concerns. This statement focuses on others.

17. A pregnant patient calls the triage nurse and says she has a burning sensation with urination. What is the best response by the nurse?

    A. "This is a sign that labor is starting soon. Get ready to come to the hospital."
    B. "You could have a urinary tract infection. Drink some cranberry juice."
    C. "You need to call your healthcare provider to make an appointment to be checked for infection."

D. "The pelvic wall is weakening, but pelvic muscle exercises can help."

Rationale:

Correct answer: C

A patient who is pregnant and develops a urinary tract infection (UTI) needs quick and aggressive antibiotic treatment to prevent acute pyelonephritis. The nurse needs to encourage the patient to notify her healthcare provider for an appointment to diagnose and treat the infection. To prevent UTI, the female patient should be taught to void before and after intercourse, clean properly after defecation (wipe from front to back), and void every two to three hours to minimize urinary stasis in the bladder.

A is incorrect because burning with urination does not indicate that labor is starting soon. Characteristic findings of the onset of labor include lightening, softening of the cervix, expulsion of the mucus plug, and regular and progressive uterine contractions.

B is incorrect because the patient needs to see the healthcare provider. Cranberry juice can help to acidify urine which can be beneficial for the patient experiencing a UTI, but proper diagnosis and prescription of antibiotics is more important.

D is incorrect because burning with urination does not occur with weakening of pelvic muscles.

18. A patient with polycystic kidney disease (PKD) is admitted to the medical unit. When assessing the patient, which finding would indicate the nurse needs to notify the healthcare provider immediately?

   A. Flank pain
   B. Periorbital edema
   C. Cloudy, bloody urine
   D. Distended abdomen

Rationale:

Correct answer: B

Polycystic kidney disease (PKD) causes cysts to grow within the kidneys and is caused by a gene mutation. Periorbital edema is a symptom of fluid retention and may be linked with hypertension. Hypertension can occur with PKD because the kidneys are not able to effectively diurese fluid, leading to increased circulatory volume. This increases the patient's risk for further kidney damage and stroke and must be assessed immediately by the healthcare provider.

A is incorrect because flank pain is due to enlarged kidneys and displacement of organs due to PKD. This is a common and expected finding and often is the reason the patient comes into the healthcare facility.

C is incorrect because cloudy, bloody urine could be due to infection or rupture of a cyst, but the circulatory issue (hypertension) is greater priority.

D is incorrect because a distended abdomen is a common finding due to enlarged kidneys and displacement of organs due to PKD.

19. The nurse has taught a patient with early polycystic kidney disease (PKD) regarding therapy with nutrition. Which patient statement demonstrates correct understanding?

    A. "I should take a laxative nightly at bedtime."
    B. "I will increase dietary fiber intake and fluid intake."
    C. "I will use salt only when I cook food myself."
    D. "Eating white bread will decrease gastrointestinal gas."

Rationale:

Correct answer: B

Polycystic kidney disease (PKD) causes cysts to grow within the kidneys and is caused by a gene mutation. PKD often leads to constipation that can be improved with fiber, exercise, and water intake.

A is incorrect because patients with PKD should use laxatives cautiously. Constipation is common with kidney disease, but if laxatives are taken regularly, this can lead to electrolyte disturbances, which can worsen kidney disease.

C is incorrect because patients with PKD should restrict their salt intake and limit salt use when cooking. Salt substitutes can be a safe way to flavor food without increasing dietary sodium intake.

D is incorrect because white bread is low in fiber. Patients with kidney disease should be encouraged to increase intake of whole grain products.

20. A 55-year-old female patient with a history of diabetes mellitus is in the clinic for the third time this year for acute pyelonephritis. When the patient asks what she can do to prevent the infections, what is the best response by the nurse?

   A. "You can test your urine every day for ketones and proteins."
   B. "Don't use sanitary napkins during your period, use tampons instead."
   C. "Increase your water intake and empty your bladder more often while awake."
   D. "Improve your blood sugar control to keep your hemoglobin A_{1c} under 9%."

Rationale:

Correct answer: C

Pyelonephritis is bacterial infection of the kidney and renal pelvis which causes kidney inflammation and can lead to scarring and failure of the kidneys. Symptoms include fever, malaise, flank pain, urinary frequency, and dysuria (pain or burning with urination). Patients who have diabetes mellitus are at increased risk for pyelonephritis due to elevated blood glucose and pH change of the urine, neuropathy, and decreased bladder tone. The nurse should suggest increased water intake (up to 3 liters daily) and more frequent voiding to prevent overgrowth of bacteria within the urinary tract. Other predisposing factors for pyelonephritis include UTI, pregnancy, tumor near the kidneys, or urinary obstruction. Antibiotics, antiseptics, IV fluids, and analgesics will be used to treat pyelonephritis.

A is incorrect because testing for ketones and proteins will not prevent pyelonephritis. Proteins and ketones are not generally found in the urine, but they are not specifically linked to infection. WBCs and nitrites in the urine are indicative of infection.

B is incorrect because using tampons instead of sanitary napkins will not prevent pyelonephritis. (Patients who have experienced toxic shock syndrome should consider using pads instead of tampons.)

D is incorrect because 9% is much too high for hemoglobin A_{1c}. Normal glycosylated hemoglobin is under 6%.

21. A patient with acute glomerulonephritis (GN) is admitted to the medical unit. When the nurse evaluates the patient, which finding would be recognized as positive response to treatment as prescribed?

    A. 7 pound weight loss over 10 days
    B. Specific gravity of urine 1.047
    C. Patient is able to expectorate secretions
    D. Blood pressure 154/86 mmHg

Rationale:

Correct answer: A

Acute glomerulonephritis (GN) is inflammation of the glomeruli, which affects filtration in the kidney. This is often caused by an immunological reaction due to an infection in another part of the body (10 days after a skin or throat infection.) GN is characterized by fever, chills, generalized edema, hypertension, fluid retention, and lung rales. A 7 pound weight loss over 10 days indicates diuresis, meaning the glomeruli are filtrating properly. This is a positive response to prescribed treatment.

B is incorrect because specific gravity of urine 1.047 is elevated and is indicative of concentrated urine, which is seen with GN. Positive response to treatment would be a specific gravity that fluctuates within normal limits (1.010-1.030).

C is incorrect because GN can cause fluid in the lungs, so if the patient is expectorating secretions, this suggests that fluid is still accumulating within the lungs. Positive response to treatment would be clear lung fields with no secretions present.

D is incorrect because blood pressure of 154/86 mmHg is high and could indicate damage to the kidneys or continuing overload of fluid. Antihypertensives are a component of treatment for GN, so a good outcome would be BP within normal limits.

22. The nurse in the surgical unit is assessing a patient with renal cell carcinoma who underwent radical nephrectomy. Blood pressure has changed from 136/92 to 102/60 mmHg, and urine output for the past hour is 20 mL. Which of the following actions should be taken by the nurse?

    A. Place the patient on the surgical incision
    B. Measure urine specific gravity

C. Administer IV pain medicine

D. Assess pulse rate and quality

Rationale:

Correct answer: D

Radical nephrectomy is removal of a kidney due to cancer, persistent infection, or anomalies. This is a "last resort" intervention when other treatments have failed. The nurse needs to assess the patient for volume depletion and shock signs, including pulse rate and quality, and notify the healthcare provider. The surgery is radical and close to the adrenal gland, risking hemorrhage risk as well as adrenal insufficiency.

A is incorrect because placing the patient on the surgical incision is inappropriate and will likely cause pain. The patient should be turned regularly, with the HOB elevated to prevent stretching and pressure on the incision.

B is incorrect because measuring specific gravity does not provide necessary data related to the drop in blood pressure.

C is incorrect because administering pain medication is not related to this situation. The question does not state that the patient is in pain, and when hypotension is present, the nurse should address that circulatory issue ahead of pain treatment. Pain post-nephrectomy is often treated with patient controlled analgesia. However, this can drop BP, so should be used cautiously.

23. The nurse in the emergency room cares for a patient admitted with a puncture wound with kidney trauma. The nurse notes abdominal tenderness and distention and blood at the urinary meatus. Which of the following orders by the healthcare provider should the nurse question?

    A. 15-minute vital signs
    B. Insertion of a urinary catheter
    C. IV fluids 125 mL/hr
    D. Type and crossmatch

Rationale:

Correct answer: B

Diagnostic testing should be performed before insertion of a urinary catheter when blood is visualized at the urinary meatus. This could indicate a torn urethra. If a catheter is needed, a suprapubic catheter can be inserted by the healthcare provider.

A is incorrect because vital signs should be monitored frequently for a patient with a puncture wound.

C is incorrect because IV fluids are appropriate for a patient who has experienced trauma. Fluids are used to restore or maintain fluid volume in a patient who is NPO or who has experienced blood loss.

D is incorrect because type and crossmatch is appropriate for a patient who has experienced trauma. This is an appropriate and safe assessment for the nurse to make prior to giving blood replacement products.

24. A patient is taught about hypertension related to kidney disease by the nurse. Which patient statement demonstrates more teaching is needed?

    A. "If I manage my blood pressure, further kidney damage can be prevented."
    B. "I should drink less during daytime hours if I have to get up at night to urinate."
    C. "I will speak with the registered dietitian about limiting protein intake."
    D. "I will take my antihypertensive medications as ordered by the healthcare provider."

Rationale:

Correct answer: B

Increased nighttime urination is not an indication to restrict daytime fluid intake. Only when necessary, the healthcare provider will prescribe fluid restriction for the patient with renal disease. Fluid intake later in the day can be decreased in order to decrease nocturnal voiding, but adequate hydration throughout the day is necessary.

A is incorrect because blood pressure management will slow progression of renal disease, indicating correct understanding.

C is incorrect because the patient prescribed limited protein intake should be referred to the registered dietitian, indicating correct understanding. The purpose of the kidney diet is to keep protein, potassium, and sodium low. Food examples include unsalted vegetables, white rice, and canned fruits. Restricted foods include beans, cereals, and citrus fruits.

D is incorrect because blood pressure management will slow progression of renal disease, indicating correct understanding.

25. A patient who underwent nephrostomy tube placement six hours ago has decreased tube drainage from 50 mL/hr to 15 mL/hr. What action should be taken by the nurse?

    A. Document urine output in the chart
    B. Report the tube is draining as expected in hand-off report
    C. Clamp the tube to prepare for removal
    D. Assess abdomen and vital signs

Rationale:

Correct answer: D

A nephrostomy tube (catheter) is placed through a flank incision into the pelvis of the kidney to drain urine into a collection bag. The tube should have consistent drainage. If the nurse notes decrease in drainage, obstruction is suspected. The nurse needs to assess the abdomen for distention and vital signs and then notify the healthcare provider.

A is incorrect because the decreased urine output warrants further assessment and is a higher priority than documentation.

B is incorrect because the tube is not draining as expected. The decrease in output indicates the tube may be obstructed and this is important information to include in the hand-off report.

C is incorrect because a nephrostomy tube should never be clamped or irrigated.

26. A patient is in the clinic for pre-renal acute kidney injury (AKI). When reviewing the patient history, which condition would the nurse consider as a cause for this patient's AKI?

    A. Pyelonephritis
    B. Myocardial infarction
    C. Bladder cancer
    D. Kidney stones

Rationale:

Correct answer: B

Pre-renal acute kidney injury (AKI) is injury that occurs to the kidneys as a result of decreased blood flow, vascular obstruction, or vascular resistance. The term *pre-renal* indicates that the cause for the kidney damage occurred in a body system before the kidney is reached. Myocardial infarction decreases blood flow to the kidneys, and therefore, reduces filtration by the kidneys.

A is incorrect because pyelonephritis causes chronic kidney disease, not pre-renal AKI.

C is incorrect because bladder cancer is post-renal, not pre-renal.

D is incorrect because kidney stones are post-renal, not pre-renal.

27. A patient who is a marathon runner is admitted to the emergency room for tachycardia. Heart rate is 115 bpm and blood pressure 82/56. The patient tells the nurse he hasn't urinated much for the last few days. Which of the following actions is priority?

    A. Encourage PO fluids immediately
    B. Start peripheral IV of 0.45% NaCl
    C. Instruct the patient drink at least 2 liters of water per day
    D. Perform an EKG

Rationale:

Correct answer: A

Tachycardia and hypotension indicate dehydration. The patient should be encouraged to drink fluids immediately to replenish depleted circulating fluid volume.

B is incorrect because starting an IV is appropriate, but 0.45 sodium chloride is hypotonic and can be detrimental to a patient who is already exhibiting signs of hypotension. This patient does not have any symptoms that necessitate NPO status, so PO fluids should be started first, with isotonic IV fluids started afterward if the symptoms don't improve.

C is incorrect because teaching the patient about daily fluid intake is not priority at this time. The nurse must select the answer that will immediately help the patient right now. Teaching about daily fluid needs can be done after the patient is stabilized or at discharge.

D is incorrect because an EKG is not needed at this time.

28. A patient admitted to the emergency room has a serum creatinine level of 2.4 mg/dL and blood urea nitrogen (BUN) of 26 mL/dL. What is the first question the nurse should ask when documenting patient history?

    A. "Have you taken aspirin, naproxen, or ibuprofen recently?"

    B. "Does anyone in your family have renal failure?"

    C. "Have you been following a low-protein diet?"

    D. "Has anyone in your family had a kidney transplant recently?"

Rationale:

Correct answer: A

The nonsteroidal anti-inflammatory drugs aspirin, naproxen, and ibuprofen are nephrotoxic and can elevate creatinine and BUN. The nurse should ask the patient about taking these medications recently. Normal adult creatinine is 0.7-1.4 mg/dL and normal BUN is 10-20 mg/dL. Both of these are tested to evaluate kidney function.

B is incorrect because family history of renal failure is not priority over current medications which may be causing the abnormal lab values.

C is incorrect because a *high* protein diet can cause elevated BUN.

D is incorrect because family history of kidney transplant is not pertinent to the situation.

29. A patient in the intensive care unit (ICU) has potassium level 6.4 mmol/L, creatinine 2.2 mg/dL, and urine output has been 325 mL/day. Which action by the nurse is priority?

    A. Put the patient on cardiac monitor

    B. Teach the patient about limiting high-potassium foods

    C. Monitor intake and output

    D. Redraw blood specimen for retesting

Rationale:

Correct answer: A

Normal potassium is 3.5-5.0 mEq/L, so this patient is extremely hyperkalemic. Normal adult creatinine is 0.7-1.4 mg/dL, so this patient has impaired renal function or severe dehydration. The urine output is extremely low (normal UP is 1-1.5 L daily). Monitoring cardiac rhythm, is priority because hyperkalemia can cause EKG changes, dysrhythmias, and cardiac arrest. Potassium-wasting diuretics may be given to increase renal clearance of excess potassium.

B is incorrect because teaching about limiting high-potassium foods is not priority until after the patient is stabilized and cardiac function is being properly monitored. Calcium gluconate or sodium bicarbonate should be available at the bedside.

C is incorrect because monitoring intake and output is not as important as monitoring cardiac rhythm.

D is incorrect because redrawing the blood specimen is not priority.

30. A patient has just had a hemodialysis catheter placed. Which of the following actions by the nurse is most appropriate?

    A. Use the line for drawing blood
    B. Monitor central venous pressure (CVP) using the line
    C. Use the line for IV medication administration
    D. Place heparin or heparin/saline dwell following hemodialysis

Rationale:

Correct answer: D

A hemodialysis catheter is a line placed for blood exchange between the body and the hemodialysis machine when the kidneys fail. Following hemodialysis, the nurse should instill heparin or heparin/saline dwell to keep the line patent. Other important nursing assessments after hemodialysis include monitoring for hemorrhage and disequilibrium syndrome (headache, confusion.) It is also important to avoid using the arm with the hemodyalisis catheter for blood pressure readings.

A is incorrect because a hemodialysis catheter should not be used for blood draws.

B is incorrect because a hemodialysis catheter cannot be used for CVP measurement. CVP is measured through a central line, such as a triple-lumen catheter. The measurement reflects the pressure in the right atrium of the heart.

C is incorrect because a hemodialysis catheter should not be used for IV medication infusion.

31. A patient in the intensive care unit (ICU) has continuous venovenous hemofiltration (CVVH) started for renal failure. Which finding by the nurse warrants immediate intervention?

  A. Blood pressure 84/48 mmHg
  B. Sodium level 136 mEq/L
  C. Potassium level 5.6 mEq/L
  D. Heart rate 94 bpm

Rationale:

Correct answer: A

Continuous venovenous hemofiltration (CVVH) is temporary hemodialysis performed continuously for patients who have low blood pressure or other contraindications for hemodialysis. CVVH is a form of continuous renal replacement therapy (CRRT). Replacement fluid is infused along with CVVH, and if there is not enough volume, then hypotension can result. The nurse trained to perform CVVH monitors for BP and fluid and electrolyte balance while performing the procedure.

B is incorrect because normal sodium level is 135-145 mEq/L.

C is incorrect because the slightly elevated potassium is expected in the patient experiencing acute kidney injury. (Normal potassium is 3.5-5.0 mEq/L.)

D is incorrect because the heart rate is within normal limits and is not concerning to the nurse.

32. The nurse on the medical-surgical unit has just received the hand-off report on four patients with chronic kidney disease (CKD). Which patient does the nurse plan on assessing first?

  E. Female patient with blood pressure 156/94 mmHg
  F. Patient exhibiting Kussmaul respirations
  G. Male patient who is experiencing itching head to toe
  H. Patient who has halitosis and stomatitis

Rationale:

Correct answer: B

Chronic kidney disease (CKD) is gradual kidney function loss over an extended period of time. A patient with CKD and Kussmaul respirations is experiencing air hunger and a worsening of the condition and breathing faster and deeper in order to blow off carbon dioxide.

A is incorrect because CKD is commonly associated with hypertension.

C is incorrect because itching is due to calcium-phosphate imbalance that is common with CKD.

D is incorrect because halitosis and stomatitis are due to uremia and ammonia formation that are common with CKD.

33. A float nurse is working with a patient who has an arteriovenous (AV) fistula in the left arm for hemodialysis. Which of the following actions by the float nurse warrants intervention by the charge nurse?

    A. Palpating access site for bruit or thrill
    B. Using the right arm for blood pressure
    C. Administering IV fluids through AV fistula
    D. Checking pulses distal to AV fistula

Rationale:

Correct answer: C

An arteriovenous (AV) fistula is formed in surgery by joining a vein and artery under the skin with a special tube. Once healed, the AV fistula is accessed for hemodialysis by placing needles in the arterial and venous sides and allowing increased blood flow during dialysis. An AV fistula should never be used for administration of IV fluids or medications, which would require intervention by the charge nurse.

A is incorrect because palpating for thrill and auscultating for bruit is appropriate assessment of an AV fistula and should be performed every eight hours.

B is incorrect because using the arm without an AV fistula is appropriate for blood pressure measurement.

D is incorrect because checking pulses distal to the AV fistula is appropriate.

34. A patient undergoing peritoneal dialysis is assessed by the nurse. The nurse notes the effluent is opaque. Which of the following actions by the nurse is priority?

    A. Warm dialysate solution in the microwave before using
    B. Sample effluent and send to the lab for evaluation
    C. Flush tubing with normal saline for patency
    D. Check peritoneal catheter for curling or kinking

Rationale:

Correct answer: B

Peritoneal dialysis uses the peritoneum as the filter for waste products and excess fluid from the blood as an alternative to hemodialysis. When effluent is opaque or cloudy, this usually indicates peritonitis, an infection of the peritoneum. The nurse should take a sample of the effluent and send it to the lab for culture and sensitivity for identification of microbes and antibiotic choice by the healthcare provider.

A is incorrect because the microwave is never used for medications of any type. The dialysate solution should be warmed to body temperature by a cycler machine or heating pad prior to peritoneal dialysis administration. Temperature of solution is unrelated to peritonitis.

C is incorrect because flushing the peritoneal dialysis tubing or catheter is unsafe and is not related to the potential infection.

D is incorrect because checking for obstruction is an appropriate routine nursing assessment when caring for a peritoneal dialysis patient but is not related to the indication of peritonitis.

35. A patient in the intensive care unit (ICU) has received a kidney transplant. Which assessment by the nurse is the most concerning?

    A. Scant urine output
    B. Temperature 99.1°F (37.3°C)
    C. Leukopenia
    D. Heartrate 122 bpm

Rationale:

Correct answer: D

Kidney transplant involves the replacement of a diseased kidney with a healthy kidney from a cadaver, identical twin, or histo-compatible donor. Tachycardia after transplantation is a sign of shock, and the patient's blood pressure must be assessed immediately. The nurse should be prepared to notify the healthcare provider immediately and push fluids.

A is incorrect because urine output is expected to be scant for days to weeks following the transplant. Hemodialysis may be needed until the implanted kidney functions well (two to three weeks after transplant).

B is incorrect because a slightly elevated temperature is common the first day post-operatively. The nurse should continue to monitor for signs of post-op infection, including a persistent elevated temperature.

C is incorrect because immunosuppressant medications are given to prevent rejection of the new kidney. A common finding is low white blood cells.

36. The home health nurse is teaching a patient about self-catheterization at home. Which of the following statements should be included by the nurse? (Select all that apply.)

    A. "Before and after self-catheterization, wash your hands well."
    B. "A large-lumen catheter should be used each time."
    C. "Lubricate the tip of the catheter before self-catheterization."
    D. "Self-catheterization should be performed every 12 hours or twice a day."
    E. "Sterile technique with sterile gloves should be utilized."
    F. "Keep a schedule for self-catheterization."

Rationale:

Correct answer: A, C, F

The patient learning about self-catheterization should be taught to wash their hands before and after the procedure, use lubrication on the catheter, and keep a schedule to prevent distention of the bladder and urinary retention that contribute to growth of bacteria.

B is incorrect because a small-lumen catheter should be used. A larger catheter is only needed if the smaller lumen catheter is unable to properly drain the urine.

D is incorrect because self-catheterization should be performed more frequently than twice a day.

E is incorrect because self-catheterization is performed utilizing clean technique.

37. A patient in the clinic has a fungal urinary tract infection (UTI). Which actions should be completed by the nurse? (Select all that apply.)

    A. Initiate antifungal treatment

    B. Assess medical history

    C. Assess for neutropenia

    D. Ask about recent travel to a foreign country

    E. Obtain a list of current medications

Rationale:

Correct answer: B, C, E

Fungal UTIs are more likely to occur in patients who have diabetes mellitus or are severely immunocompromised. The fungal infection usually spreads from the GI tract or from fungus presence on a urinary catheter and can also develop secondary to antibiotic treatment for a bacterial infection. The nurse should assess medical history and current medications to determine the cause of the fungal infection. Not all fungal UTIs require medical treatment, as they often are asymptomatic and will clear up on their own. However, a neutropenic patient is a candidate for antifungal medication, so assessing for neutropenia is important.

A is incorrect because antifungal treatment is not indicated unless the patient is symptomatic, neutropenic, has a renal allograft, or is high-risk.

D is incorrect because foreign country travel is not related to development of fungal UTI.

38. A patient who has had calcium phosphate kidney stones is educated by the nurse. Which of the following statements regarding dietary teaching does the nurse include? (Select all that apply.)

    A. "Limit animal protein intake."

    B. "Reduce sodium intake and read nutrition labels."

C. "Avoid black tea, rhubarb, and spinach."

D. "Drink beer or white wine rather than red wine."

E. "Reduce or avoid dairy products."

Rationale:

Correct answer: A, B, E

Patients who experience calcium phosphate kidney stones should be educated about limiting animal protein intake, sodium intake, and calcium. (Sodium increases calcium in the urine.)

C is incorrect because black tea, rhubarb, and spinach should be avoided by those with calcium oxalate stones, not calcium phosphate stones.

D is incorrect because red wine should be avoided by those with uric acid stones, not calcium phosphate stones.

39. The patient who had a urinary calculus lithotripsy treatment is educated by the nurse. Which of the following statements does the nurse include in discharge teaching? (Select all that apply.)

A. "Finish your antibiotics even if you feel better."

B. "Drink 2-3 liters of water each day."

C. "Bruising on your back could take several weeks to get better."

D. "Notify your healthcare provider if you notice any blood in your urine."

E. "Pain and difficulty urinating are common."

Rationale:

Correct answer: A, B, C

Extracorporeal shock wave lithotripsy is the use of high energy sound waves through the skin to break down kidney stones into smaller pieces that are able to pass through the ureters and into the bladder to be eliminated with voiding. Prophylactic antibiotics should be taken until the course is completed to prevent a urinary tract infection and urosepsis. The patient should drink at least 2-3 liters of water daily to maintain adequate hydration and prevent the formation of more kidney stones. The bruising that results from lithotripsy takes several weeks to improve.

D is incorrect because blood in urine is common after lithotripsy and this is not an indication of a complication.

E is incorrect because pain and difficulty urinating may be indications of infection or persistent kidney stones and these findings should be reported to the healthcare provider.

40. A female patient is learning about stress incontinence and pelvic muscle exercises from the nurse. Which of the following statements should be included by the nurse? (Select all that apply.)

   A. "Pelvic muscles are used when starting and stopping the urine stream."
   B. "Tighten the pelvic muscles for ten seconds then relax for ten seconds."
   C. "Perform pelvic muscle exercises when seated upright with feet on the floor."
   D. "Do these exercises for a couple of days, and your urine control will get better."
   E. "Your pelvic muscles, like other muscles, strengthen with contraction."

Rationale:

Correct answer: A, B, E

The nurse should include teaching the patient that the purpose of pelvic floor muscles is for stopping and starting urine stream. Muscles are strengthened with contraction and relaxation for ten seconds each time.

C is incorrect because pelvic muscle exercises should be done in multiple positions: lying down, sitting up, and standing, for maximum effect.

D is incorrect because it takes several weeks for improvement in urine control to be achieved.

NCLEX-RN – MED-SURG: INTEGUMENTARY – 25 QUESTIONS

1. The nurse in the burn unit is providing discharge instructions for a patient who received a skin graft due to deep partial thickness burns from a work accident at a chemical plant. Which instruction does the nurse include that is most important for the patient to remember?

    A. Continue physical therapy
    B. Maintain a low-protein, high-fiber diet
    C. Protect the skin graft from direct sunlight
    D. Use cosmetic camouflage techniques

Rationale:

Correct answer: C

A skin graft is a flap of donor skin either from another part of the body or from another person to cover exposed tissue as the result of injury, infection, or burn. In order to prevent burning and sloughing of the new skin graft, it must be protected from direct sunlight.

A is incorrect because physical therapy is important but not most important.

B is incorrect because burn patients need a high-protein, high-calorie diet. High-fiber diet is indicated for patients at risk for constipation, not necessarily burn patients.

D is incorrect because cosmetic camouflage creams are used to decrease the visibility of scarring from burns, but this is not the nurse's main concern. This is a psychosocial issue. Preventing the newly growing tissue at the burn site from sunlight is a greater physical concern.

2. A patient is in the clinic for treatment of herpes zoster (shingles). When assessing the patient, which characteristics would the nurse expect to find?

    A. Clustered skin vesicles
    B. Generalized rash on the body
    C. Small blue-white spots with red base
    D. Fiery red, edematous rash to the cheeks

Rationale:

Correct answer: A

Herpes zoster (shingles) is the reactivated form of varicella zoster (chicken pox) from the latent state that is characterized by red skin rash with clustered skin vesicles. The rash is painful and contagious and treated with corticosteroids. Medications such as acyclovir are prescribed for treatment. It is important for the nurse to obtain a baseline CBC and check renal function while on this medication. Remind clients that they are contagious when lesions are open and draining. Active shingles in the hospital requires airborne precautions.

B is incorrect because herpes zoster is not characterized by a generalized rash.

C is incorrect because herpes zoster is not characterized by small blue-white spots with red base. This describes Koplik's spots, which occur on the inside of the cheeks and inner surface of lower lip during the incubation of measles.

D is incorrect because herpes zoster is not characterized by a fiery red, edematous rash to the cheeks. This is a symptom of Fifth's Disease.

3. A patient is admitted to the emergency room for frostbite to the toes. When assessing the patient's toes, which of the following characteristics would the nurse expect to find?

    A. Pink, edematous toes
    B. Bright red skin and nail beds edematous
    C. Hemorrhagic vesicles, evolving into necrotic ulcers
    D. White skin, insensitive to touch

Rationale:

Correct answer: D

Frostbite is an injury that involves the freezing of the skin and underlying tissues. Skin that is frostbitten first becomes very cold and red, then numb, hard, white or blue in color, and insensitive to touch.

A is incorrect because pink skin and edema are not characteristic of frostbite.

B is incorrect because bright red skin and edematous nailbeds are not characteristic of frostbite.

C is incorrect because these are signs of ecthyma gangrenosum, an infectious complication accompanied by pseudomonas sepsis often seen in immunocompromised patients.

4. The nurse in the clinic is assessing the skin of a patient and notes the soft-tissue folds surrounding the nails are inflamed. Which question by the nurse would return the most useful information regarding the possible cause of symptoms?

    A. "What is your profession?"
    B. "Do you get professional manicures?"
    C. "Have you been diagnosed with myasthenia gravis?"
    D. "Have you recently had a fungal infection?"

Rationale:

Correct answer: A

Patients who have frequent exposure to water (including homemakers, housekeepers, laundry workers, and bartenders) are commonly diagnosed with chronic paronychia. This condition is characterized by erythema, swelling, and tenderness of the nail folds. If the nurse determines that the patient's profession is the cause of this condition, the nurse can teach the patient proper skin and nail care to prevent the infection from becoming recurrent or chronic.

B is incorrect because asking about professional manicures would not be most useful. Improper manicure technique and decreased equipment disinfection time between clients can lead to micro-trauma and infections.

C is incorrect because myasthenia gravis does not cause chronic paronychia. Myasthenia gravis is a progressive neuro-muscular disease which causes muscle weakness that descends down the body.

D is incorrect because chronic paronychia is more likely due to bacterial contamination than to fungal infection.

5. A patient admitted to the medical-surgical unit has ecchymosis noted to both arms by the nurse. What is the first question the nurse should ask?

    A. "Do you use lotion on your skin?"
    B. "Is there a family history of bruising?"
    C. "Are your arms itching?"
    D. "What medications are you currently taking?"

Rationale:

Correct answer: D

Ecchymosis is a discoloration of skin usually caused by bruising. Some medications that can cause ecchymosis (or easy bruising) including corticosteroids, aspirin, and warfarin. Assessing for current medications is a part of the initial nursing assessment and is important before asking more specific questions.

A is incorrect because use of lotion does not contribute to ecchymosis.

B is incorrect because ecchymosis is not genetically inherited.

C is incorrect because ecchymosis does not typically cause itching.

6. An overweight female patient is concerned about a rash beneath her breasts. When the nurse teaches the patient about caring for the skin, which patient statement demonstrates good understanding?

    A. "Fluid overload probably caused this rash."
    B. "I will wash the area with antibacterial soap daily."
    C. "Powder can be used to keep the skin underneath my breasts dry."
    D. "I will be scheduling a mammogram soon."

Rationale:

Correct answer: C

Excessive moisture usually causes rashes located in skinfolds, including the groin, the axillae, and beneath the breasts, especially in patients who are overweight or obese. The patient should keep the area as dry as possible, and powder can be applied to dry skin to prevent moisture from accumulating throughout the day.

A is incorrect because fluid overload is not related to skinfold rash and this statement by the patient does not indicate an understanding of how to properly care for the skin.

B is incorrect because antibacterial soap is not necessary for skin hygiene. Antibacterial soap prevents infection, but this rash is not likely infectious in nature.

D is incorrect because breast cancer is not related to skinfold rash. Mammograms are indicated for women beginning at the age of 40 or for those who detect a lump or tenderness in the breasts or axillae. Some doctors will order annual mammograms for women younger than 40 who have a family history of breast cancer.

7. The nurse is assessing the lower extremities of a patient admitted to the medical-surgical unit. When the nurse notes one lower extremity is cool to the touch and pale, what is the next assessment the nurse should perform?

    A. Inquire about family history of disorders of the skin
    B. Palpate bilateral pedal pulses
    C. Check for Homans' sign
    D. Assess skin turgor

Rationale:

Correct answer: B

Decreased temperature in the skin with pallor localized to one area can indicate vascular flow interference, such as a thrombus. Pedal pulses should be palpated bilaterally to check for distal circulation. The suspected leg's pulses should be compared to the unaffected leg. If the lower extremity does not have adequate blood flow, the limb is threatened, and the healthcare provider must be notified immediately.

A is incorrect because family history of skin disorder is not priority over blood flow.

C is incorrect because Homans' sign screens for deep vein thrombosis (DVT) and is not accurate. Some research now shows that checking for Homans' sign can actually cause dislodgement of a thrombus from the leg, causing an embolus to move through the circulation, so it is not widely practiced anymore.

D is incorrect because skin turgor assesses fluid status. Poor skin turgor can indicate dehydration. This patient is exhibiting signs of impaired circulation, not dehydration.

8. A patient in the clinic has a history of chronic skin disorder. Which of the following demonstrates effective coping related to the disorder?

    A. Clean nails and hair
    B. Poor eye contact
    C. Disheveled appearance
    D. Scarf draped over the face

Rationale:

Correct answer: A

Psychosocial assessment should be performed to determine effective coping with a chronic skin disorder. The patient is effectively coping if the nails and hair appear clean.

B is incorrect because poor eye contact is a sign of anxiety and does not demonstrate effective coping.

C is incorrect because disheveled appearance does not demonstrate effective coping. People with chronic skin disorders such as "Picking disorder" often appear unkempt, unclean, and have uneven fingernails with areas of skin that has been picked away from various body locations, mostly the face and hands.

D is incorrect because a scarf draped over the face can indicate either religious preference or anxiety and embarrassment, not effective coping.

9. The nurse on the medical-surgical unit is caring for four patients. Which patient has the greatest risk of developing a pressure ulcer?

    A. 40-year-old with IV antibiotics prescribed for pneumonia
    B. 28-year-old with a fractured femur, on bedrest, in skeletal suspension traction
    C. 70-year-old admitted with incontinence and hemi-paralysis
    D. 72-year-old who ambulates with a walker

Rationale:

Correct answer: C

Pressure ulcers are breakdown of the skin and subcutaneous layers due to decreased circulation, constant moisture, decreased sensation, and constant pressure among many other factors. Immobility related to paralysis and incontinence are significant risk factors for pressure ulcers.

A is incorrect because the patient admitted for pneumonia is not at risk for pressure ulcers. Pneumonia patients have decreased lung capacity and may experience fatigue, but the nurse will ambulate as tolerated and this patient is capable of adjusting position in bed to relieve pressure. Antibiotics are not a risk for pressure ulcers.

B is incorrect because the patient on bedrest in skeletal suspension traction is at slight risk for pressure ulcers, but this is temporary. Traction prepares patients for surgery with goals to be out of bed and ambulatory after the procedure.

D is incorrect because the patient who ambulates with a walker is not at risk for pressure ulcers.

10. A patient in the intensive care unit (ICU) has a Stage III pressure ulcer on the left heel. What is the first action the nurse should take?

    A. Draw blood work to assess total protein, albumin, and prealbumin
    B. Obtain a wound culture
    C. Place the patient on bedrest and tell the patient to keep the foot elevated
    D. Assess left lower extremity for temperature, skin color, and pulses

Rationale:

Correct answer: D

Pressure ulcers are breakdown of the skin and subcutaneous layers due to decreased circulation, constant moisture, decreased sensation, and constant pressure, among many other factors. The nurse needs to assess the lower extremity for temperature, skin color, and pulses to determine if there is an obstruction to arterial blood flow.

A is incorrect because total protein, albumin, and prealbumin are assessed after blood flow. Assessing current circulatory status at the bedside is a greater priority than drawing labs. (These labs will indicate nutritional status and healing ability.)

B is incorrect because a wound culture is only performed if there is drainage, odor, or suspicion of infection; culture is not priority or routine when caring for pressure ulcer.

C is incorrect because elevating the extremity decreases blood flow to the area and it indicated for swelling, not pressure ulcer.

11. The nurse is caring for four patients on the medical unit. Which patient needs to be evaluated for wound infection?

    A. Patient who has blood cultures pending

    B. Patient whose wound has a moderate amount of thin, serous drainage

    C. Patient whose white blood cell count was 24,000/mm³ this morning

    D. Patient whose wound is decreasing in size

Rationale:

Correct answer: C

Normal white blood cell (WBC) count is 4,500 to 10,000/mm³. The WBCs are elevated at 24,000/mm³, so this patient should be assessed for wound infection.

A is incorrect because pending blood cultures are not an indication of wound infection.

B is incorrect because thin, serous drainage from a wound is not an indication of wound infection. Signs of infection include elevated WBCs, purulent drainage, yellow- or green-colored drainage, foul odor, and increased pain at the wound site.

D is incorrect because a wound decreasing in size is a sign of improvement, not infection.

12. A patient in the clinic has multiple lesions of the skin. Which of the following lesions should be evaluated by the nurse first?

    A. Beige freckles on the hands and arms

    B. Lower leg mole, irregular shape, blue with white specks

    C. Cluster of pustules to the left axilla

    D. Red, thick pustules with white scales on the upper legs

Rationale:

Correct answer: B

A mole that is irregular and blue with white specks fits criteria for possibly being precancerous or cancerous. The criteria for cancer include variation of color in one lesion, irregular border, size greater than 6mm, change in appearance or new symptom. This patient may need an oncology consult and biopsy.

A is incorrect because freckles are common and benign.

C is incorrect because pustules indicate possible infection, but the abnormal mole is the greatest concern because of the risk for cancer.

D is incorrect because red, thick pustules with white scales are a symptom of psoriasis and are not priority. Psoriasis, a treatable, autoimmune, chronic skin disorder, is not a medical emergency.

13. The nurse is preparing to assess a patient with psoriasis. What is the first action the nurse should take?

    A. Don gloves and isolation gown
    B. Shake hands and introduce self
    C. Assess for infection
    D. Ask if the patient could be pregnant

Rationale:

Correct answer: B

Psoriasis is red, raised, and scaly patches most commonly on the skin on the elbows, knees, and scalp and caused by autoimmune disease. Patients who have lesions caused by psoriasis often are self-conscious about their skin, so the nurse should shake hands and touch the patient before putting on gloves in order to establish rapport. Therapeutic touch is a component of establishing a healthy nurse-client relationship.

A is incorrect because donning gloves and isolation gown is not necessary as psoriasis is not contagious. Psoriasis is an autoimmune, chronic skin disorder that is characterized by periods of exacerbation. When the psoriasis patient is on immunosuppressant medications, they may be more susceptible to infection, but gloves and gown are not necessary.

C is incorrect because psoriasis is not infectious. The nurse does not need to assess for infections unless symptoms of infection are present or if the nurse has confirmed the patient is taking immunosuppressant medications.

D is incorrect because assessing for pregnancy is done after establishing rapport.

14. The nurse is teaching the spouse of a patient whose Braden Scale is 9. Which of the following questions does the nurse include when assessing coping needs?

    A. "Do you have trouble using a bedpan for your spouse at home?"

    B. "How do you cope with provision of care at home?"

    C. "How are you preventing pediculosis?"

    D. "Do you share the bed with your spouse?"

Rationale:

Correct answer: B

The Braden Scale for Predicting Pressure Sore Risk is used to assess sensory perception, activity, mobility, moisture, nutrition, and friction/shear. Score ranges from 6 (highest risk) to 23 (lowest risk) and includes preventive interventions for each range of scores. The patient with Braden Scale of 9 is at a high risk and requires a great deal of assistance for prevention of skin breakdown. This disrupts family routines and adds stress, so the nurse should assess spousal feelings and coping strategies while providing support.

A is incorrect because discussion of toileting practices does not assess the spouse's coping ability. Helping a family member with bedpan toileting can be difficult and requires education about safety and infection control.

C is incorrect because preventing pediculosis practices does not assess the spouse's coping ability. Measures to prevent lice include preventing head-to-head contact and not sharing clothing or towels.

D is incorrect because assessing sleeping arrangements does not assess the spouse's coping ability. Patients with risk for pressure ulcers may need individualized sleeping arrangements at home (wedge pillows, rotating beds) that may make it difficult to share a bed with their spouse.

15. The nurse on the long-term care unit is caring for a patient with a deep wound to the right lower extremity. A wet-to-damp dressing is utilized to treat the wound. Which of the following interventions does the nurse need to include in the plan of care?

A. Change dressing every six hours

B. Assess wound bed daily

C. Change dressing when saturated

D. Notify the healthcare provider when decreased fluid drainage is noted from the dressing

Rationale:

Correct answer: A

Wet-to-damp dressings are utilized for debridement of wounds. Maximum debridement is achieved when the dressing is changed every four to six hours.

B is incorrect because assessing the wound bed daily is not frequent enough. The wound should be assessed with every dressing change (four times daily).

C is incorrect because the wound dressing should be changed every four to six hours even if the dressing is not saturated. A wound that leaks a lot of fluid may need to be changed more frequently.

D is incorrect because decreased fluid drainage is a sign of improvement, and the healthcare provider does not need to be notified.

16. The oncology nurse is assessing the skin of an older adult in the clinic. Which of the following findings would require an immediate call to the healthcare provider? (Select all that apply.)

A. Excessive moisture to axilla

B. Thinning of the hair

C. Increase of fungal presence in toenails

D. Multicolored lesion

E. Spider veins to lower extremities

F. Dark, 6mm asymmetric lesion to forehead

Rationale:

Correct answer: C, D, F

The criteria for cancer include variation of color in one lesion, irregular border, size greater than 6mm, and change in appearance or new symptom. The multicolored lesion and the dark, 6mm asymmetric forehead lesion require immediate referral for cancer risk. Fungal infection in the toes is not a normal finding either.

A is incorrect because excessive moisture to axilla does not require referral for oncology services.

B is incorrect because hair thinning increase does not require referral. Thin hair is common and expected in older adults.

E is incorrect because spider veins are common and do not pose significant threat. This finding does not require referral.

17. The nurse is caring for a patient who has a non-healing wound. Which of the following focused assessments does the nurse perform for development of the plan of nursing care? (Select all that apply.)

    A. Height and weight
    B. Allergies
    C. Alcohol use
    D. Prealbumin lab results
    E. Liver enzyme lab results

Rationale:

Correct answer: A, B, C, D

Wound healing is largely dependent upon nutritional status, so the nurse needs to assess serum prealbumin levels. Height/weight and alcohol use will also help determine nutritional needs. The patient with a non-healing wound needs a high-protein and high-calorie diet to contribute to healing. A non-healing wound may require the use of additional antibiotics, so assessing for allergies is important as well.

E is incorrect because liver enzyme results does not provide wound healing information.

18. The nurse in the oncology clinic is teaching a patient how to perform self-examination of the skin monthly. Which of the following statements does the nurse include? (Select all that apply.)

    A. "Look for irregular borders and asymmetry."

B. "Look for color variations."

C. "Examine lesion distribution over body sections."

D. "Expect some edema and swelling."

E. "Focus on itchy skin areas."

Rationale:

Correct answer: A, B, C

The criteria for cancer include variation of color in one lesion, irregular border, size greater than 6mm, and change in appearance or new symptom. The patient should be taught to look for these characteristics by examining one body section at a time, with every skin assessment.

D is incorrect because edema and swelling of tissues is not expected and should be reported to the healthcare provider.

E is incorrect because itchy skin areas should not be the focus of skin assessment. The patient should be taught to perform a thorough skin assessment, even on non-itchy areas, because areas of concern may not necessarily be itchy.

19. The nurse is caring for patients on the long-term care unit who have wounds. Which of the following wounds are paired appropriately with their treatment? (Select all that apply.)

A. Heel ulcer with necrosis: whirlpool treatment

B. Eschar-covered ulcer to the sacrum: surgical debridement

C. Sunburn and erythema: 20-minute warm water soak

D. Urticaria: wet-to-dry dressing

E. Sacral ulcer with purulent drainage: transparent film dressing

Rationale:

Correct answer: A, B

Necrotic tissue must be removed in order to assist with tissue healing. Whirlpool treatment is appropriate for removing areas of pressure ulcer necrosis. Eschar usually requires surgical debridement for wound healing.

C is incorrect because warm water is not recommended for erythema and sunburn. Cool water and NSAIDs are appropriate interventions for sunburn. Avoidance of further sun exposure is also recommended.

D is incorrect because wet-to-dry dressing is not recommended for urticarial (hives.) Urticaria involves intensely pruritic, raised wheals and is treated with antihistamines. The nurse should educate the patient about avoiding triggers.

E is incorrect because transparent film dressing is not recommended for pressure ulcers, which are already presenting with drainage. Appropriate dressings are an essential component of pressure ulcer care. Transparent film dressings are to be used preventatively for skin areas that are at risk for friction injury or injury from tape. A pressure ulcer that is draining purulently requires a silver-impregnated dressing.

20. The nurse is caring for a patient who is immobilized on bedrest after spinal fusion surgery. In order to prevent pressure ulcers, which of the following interventions does the nurse include? (Select all that apply.)

   A. Small pillow placed between bony surfaces
   B. Head of the bed elevated to 45 degrees
   C. Limit proteins and fluids
   D. Lift sheet for repositioning
   E. Reposition in the chair every two hours
   F. Elevate heels off the bed

Rationale:

Correct answer: A, D, F

Pressure ulcers are breakdown of the skin and subcutaneous skin layers due to decreased circulation, constant moisture, decreased sensation, and constant pressure, among other factors. A small pillow between bony surfaces helps reduce the pressure between those surfaces (such as the knees when the patient is in a side-lying position). The lift sheet (draw sheet) is smaller than the top and bottom sheet of the bed. It is placed flat on top of the bottom sheet, horizontally across the bed underneath the patient. The lift sheet absorbs moisture from the patient and helps keep the bottom linens dry. It can also be used to help move the patient in bed, preventing shear. The lift sheet may need to be changed more often than the top or bottom sheet. Elevation of heels off the bed surface prevent pressure on the bottoms of the heels, preventing of pressure ulcers.

B is incorrect because elevating the head of bed more than 30 degrees will increase pelvic soft tissue pressure and may contribute to pressure ulcers.

C is incorrect because tissue integrity is maintained with adequate fluid and protein intake.

E is incorrect because this patient is on bedrest and should not be in a chair. Patients in the chair should be repositioned every hour.

21. The nurse is preparing to admit a patient with disseminated herpes zoster. Which of the following actions should be taken by the nurse? (Select all that apply.)

   A. Choose a room with negative pressure isolation
   B. Assess staff vaccination for or history of chicken pox
   C. Review healthcare provider orders for analgesia
   D. Choose an immune suppressed roommate
   E. Stock gloves in the room

Rationale:

Correct answer: A, B, C, E

Herpes zoster (shingles) is the reactivated form of varicella zoster (chicken pox) from the latent state that is characterized by red skin rash with clustered skin vesicles. The rash is painful and contagious. Disseminated herpes zoster requires standard precautions, airborne, and contact precautions until lesions are dry and crusted. Airborne precautions require a negative pressure isolation room. Staff members who have not had chicken pox or been vaccinated against it are at increased risk of infection with herpes zoster. The admission orders should be reviewed for analgesia. Healthcare providers will don PPE outside the room of a patient with airborne precautions, and additional gloves should also be stocked in the room.

D is incorrect because the patient with herpes zoster should not have a roommate. Patients on airborne precautions are not placed with roommates. Negative pressure isolation rooms are single rooms, generally at the end of the hallway. Immunocompromised patients should not be placed with patients who have infection of any kind.

22. The nurse is caring for several older patients at a long-term acute care hospital. In order to prevent skin breakdown, which of the following interventions does the nurse implement? (Select all that apply.)

    A. Lift sheet for repositioning in bed
    B. Avoid tape with dressing application
    C. Avoid therapy with the whirlpool
    D. Loose dressings applied to wounds
    E. Pressure-relieving devices

Rationale:

Correct answer: A, B, E

Pressure ulcers and skin breakdown are breakdown of the skin and subcutaneous layers due to decreased circulation, constant moisture, decreased sensation, and constant pressure, among many other factors. Lift sheets for repositioning reduce shear. An alternative to using tape for dressings is elastic retaining nets (such as Curad) which can be used to keep dressings in place without causing the irritation from tape. Pressure-relieving devices such as a foam mattress-topper, air-fluidized support, and sheepskin overlay all can contribute to reduction of skin breakdown incidences.

C is incorrect because there are no contraindications to whirlpool therapy for older patients.

D is incorrect because dressings should be applied per healthcare provider orders to provide treatment and not restrict blood flow.

23. A patient is in the clinic for increased psoriatic lesions. Which of the following questions does the nurse ask in order to identify triggers for worsening of psoriatic lesions? (Select all that apply.)

    A. "Have you been eating chocolate recently?"
    B. "Have you been experiencing increased stress recently?"
    C. "Have you used a public shower recently?"
    D. "Have you travelled internationally recently?"
    E. "Have you experienced other health problems recently?"
    F. "Have you had any medication changes recently?"

Rationale:

Correct answer: B, E, F

Psoriasis is red, raised, and scaly patches on the skin, most commonly on the elbows, knees, and scalp and caused by autoimmune disease. Several factors that can trigger worsening of symptoms in patients with autoimmune diseases include increased stress, other psychological factors, systemic medical problems, certain medications, and other health factors.

A is incorrect because chocolate does not trigger worsening of psoriatic lesions.

C is incorrect because public showers do not trigger worsening of psoriatic lesions. Public shower floors may contain bacteria, dead skin cells, hair, body fluids, and other microorganisms that contributes to communicable diseases such as tinea pedis (the fungus that causes athlete's foot), but they do not trigger autoimmune flare-ups.

D is incorrect because international travel does not trigger worsening of psoriatic lesions.

24. The nurse is working with an unlicensed assistive personnel (UAP) to care for a patient with open skin lesions. When delegating hygiene care to the UAP, which statements does the nurse include? (Select all that apply.)

    A. "Wash your hands before providing care."
    B. "Wear gloves to bathe the patient."
    C. "Assess for skin breakdown during bathing."
    D. "While the skin is still wet, apply lotion to the lesions."
    E. "Gently scrub the lesions with a damp cloth to help with debridement."

Rationale:

Correct answer: A, B

Standard Precautions should always be followed when caring for patients with open skin lesions. Hand hygiene and wearing gloves are part of Standard Precautions and are appropriate for hygiene care. Gloves are necessary any time a healthcare worker may come into contact with body fluids such as wound exudate from open lesions, urine, blood, stool, sputum, oral mucous, or other mucous membranes.

C is incorrect because skin assessment is the responsibility of the nurse. Assessment is not within the scope of practice for a UAP.

D is incorrect because lotion should not be applied to open skin lesions. If the UAP is going to apply lotion to a patient, the skin should be thoroughly dried first.

E is incorrect because open skin lesions should not be scrubbed. If wound debridement is required, this is the responsibility of the RN.

25. A patient with eczematous dermatitis calls the nurse to report pain and itching from the eczema. Which of the following non-pharmacologic comfort measures does the nurse instruct the patient to implement at home? (Select all that apply.)

    A. Moist, cool compresses
    B. Topical corticosteroids
    C. Heating pad
    D. Cornstarch in a tepid bath
    E. Back rub using baby oil

Rationale:

Correct answer: A, D

Eczematous dermatitis, or atopic dermatitis, is a red rash that evolves rapidly and is blistered and swollen, progressing to hardened, dry flaking skin on the face, upper chest, antecubital fossa, and popliteal fossa. The comfort measure goal is decreasing inflammation and debridement of crusts and scales. Moist, cool compresses and cornstarch in a tepid bath can all relieve pain associated with eczematous dermatitis.

B is incorrect because topical corticosteroids are not a non-pharmacologic comfort measure. (Topical steroids and antihistamines are often used to treat eczema.)

C is incorrect because a heating pad will exacerbate inflammation and pain. Patients with eczema should be taught to avoid prolonged hot baths or showers, clothing that is irritating (rough/wool), or clothing that is too tight and promotes sweating.

E is incorrect because baby oil is not appropriate for eczematous dermatitis. Evening primrose oil is an herbal option that is safe for treating eczema.

NCLEX-RN – MED-SURG: NEUROLOGICAL – 39 QUESTIONS

1. A patient with a fracture at C6 is admitted to the trauma intensive care unit. When assessing for neurogenic shock, which of the following would the nurse expect to find?

    A. Hyperactive reflexes below C6

    B. Involuntary spastic movement of extremities

    C. Hypotension, bradycardia, warm and pink extremities

    D. Lack of sensation and movement below C6

Rationale:

Correct answer: C

Shock is a life-threatening condition in which there is not enough blood flow through the body. Neurogenic shock is caused by the sudden loss of sympathetic nervous system signals that normally maintain muscle tone in blood vessel walls. The blood vessels become relaxed and dilated, causing blood to pool in the venous system and general drop in blood pressure. Spinal cord injury is damage that occurs from trauma that affects strength and sensation as well as body function below where the injury occurs. Neurogenic shock is manifested by bradycardia, hypotension, and vasodilation with warm skin.

A is incorrect because hyperactive reflexes will not be present during this stage following spinal cord injury. Reflexes below the level of the injury will be decreased or absent.

B is incorrect because involuntary spastic movement will not necessarily be present during this stage following spinal cord injury, and this is not related to neurogenic shock.

D is incorrect because although lack of sensation and movement occur with spinal cord injury, this is not descriptive of the expected nursing assessment related to neurogenic shock.

2. The nurse admits a 33-year-old male patient after a motor vehicle accident with injury to the spinal cord that left him with paraplegia and a neurogenic spastic bladder. Which intervention should the nurse include when caring for this patient?

   A. Teach Crede method
   B. Teach self-catheterization
   C. After void, catheterize for residual
   D. Assist to the toilet every two hours

Rationale:

Correct answer: B

Spinal cord injury is damage that occurs from trauma that affects strength and sensation as well as body function below where the injury occurs. The patient has a spastic bladder which responds to overstretching with emptying, so intermittent self-catheterization is appropriate to teach this patient to prevent incontinence. This is a clean process which should be done at regular intervals, every four to six hours, removing 350-400 mL or urine each time.

A is incorrect because the Crede method is the manual expression of urine from the bladder and is not safe for long-term use in paralyzed patients, especially men. (The Crede method is recommended for flaccid bladder, not neurogenic spastic bladder.)

C is incorrect because catheterization after voiding will not prevent incontinence.

D is incorrect because assisting to the toilet every two hours will not help a bladder that does not empty.

3. The nurse cares for a female patient admitted to the trauma unit 10 days ago with a T2 spinal cord injury from a fall off a horse. The patient tells the nurse, "I want to be transferred to a facility where the staff are more knowledgeable." What is the best action by the nurse?

   A. Inform the patient that derogatory communication towards the staff is not tolerated.
   B. Request that the patient participate in creating plan of care
   C. Continue to provide care and reassure the patient she is receiving the best care possible
   D. Inform the patient that all nursing staff are evaluated for competency

Rationale:

Correct answer: B

Spinal cord injury is damage that occurs from trauma that affects strength and sensation as well as body function below where the injury occurs. The patient is experiencing the anger phase in the grief process, as demonstrated by the behavior. The nurse should involve the patient in the plan of care and continue the dialogue to allow the patient to express her feelings.

A is incorrect because this is non-therapeutic. The nurse should recognize the patient's feelings as a normal part of the grieving process and allow the patient to express anger.

C is incorrect because this action dismisses the patient's comments. This can lead to worsened anger and feelings of helplessness. The nurse is responsible for empowering the patient to participate in her care.

D is incorrect because this is a form of defensive communication, which is non-therapeutic. Informing the patient about staff competence is not helpful and does not address the feelings of anger.

4. The nurse is caring for a patient with paraplegia at the T4 level due to a history of a motor vehicle accident. Which of the following interventions should the nurse perform to prevent autonomic dysreflexia in this patient?

   A. Support high-protein diet
   B. Discuss sexuality and fertility options
   C. Plan a bowel program
   D. Teach quad coughing

Rationale:

Correct answer: C

Autonomic dysreflexia (also known as autonomic hyperreflexia) occurs in patients with spinal cord injury above T6. Symptoms include uncontrolled hypertension, pounding headache, profuse sweating, nasal congestion, and bradycardia. If untreated, autonomic dysreflexia can lead to seizures, pulmonary edema, myocardial infarction, hemorrhage, and death. A routine bowel program can help prevent fecal impaction, which is the primary cause of autonomic dysreflexia. Other causes include bladder distention, unrelieved pain, or tactile stimulation (clothing too tight, wrinkles in linens).

A is incorrect because a high-protein diet will promote healing but will not prevent autonomic dysreflexia.

B is incorrect because discussion of sexuality and fertility options is important for the spinal injury patient, but it is unrelated to autonomic dysreflexia.

D is incorrect because coughing will not prevent autonomic dysreflexia. Quad coughing is assisted coughing to help spinal cord injury patients cough with enough force to expectorate secretions.

5. A 35-year-old patient has been transferred home from a rehabilitation facility after spinal cord injury. When the home health nurse visits, the spouse is noted to be performing many tasks for the patient that were self-managed in rehabilitation. What is the most appropriate intervention by the nurse?

    A. Remind the patient that independence is important for daily activities
    B. Inform the spouse of the importance of allowing the patient to perform independently
    C. Develop a care plan for increased independence with the patient and spouse
    D. Affirm the importance of the spouse's involvement and encourage the spouse to continue assistance with care

Rationale:

Correct answer: C

Spinal cord injury impairs an individual's sensation, movement, and function below the level of the injury. Spinal cord injury affects both the patient and the family members and often leads to a grieving process over the loss of function and independent lifestyle. The optimal care plan includes both the patient and the spouse.

A is incorrect because reminding the patient about independence will not necessarily change the spouse's behavior.

B is incorrect because involving care partners in assisting with care is important. The nurse must empower the patient to be independent, but also to recognize the spouse's need to help.

D is incorrect because this does not promote any independence for the patient and can lead to dependency.

6. The nurse admits a 35-year-old patient to the neurological unit with a C5 spinal cord injury 12 hours ago. Which of the following nursing interventions is priority for this patient?

    A. Teach the patient about the use of assistive feeding devices
    B. Respiratory assessment
    C. Application of compression devices to lower extremities
    D. Methylprednisolone infusion administration

Rationale:

Correct answer: B

A spinal cord injury at the level of C5 may initially impair the respiratory system due to edema of the spinal cord. Edema surrounding the spinal cord injury could lead to damage at the C4 level and above, so respiratory assessment is priority.

A is incorrect because respiratory monitoring and support is more important 12 hours after the injury. Once stabilized, the C5 injury patient will likely have some bicep control, neck movement, and partial shoulder strength. The patient will be able to power an electric wheelchair and use assistive feeding devices, depending on stability of the respiratory system.

C is incorrect because compression devices are important to promote circulation and prevent clot formation, but this is not a higher priority than respiratory assessment.

D is incorrect because methylprednisolone is no longer recommended for spinal cord injury treatment.

7. The nurse admits a patient with a history of spinal cord injury at level T3 for sacral ulcers. The patient tells the nurse that they have a headache and feels they may vomit. What is the first action the nurse should take?

    A. Check for fecal impaction
    B. Administer prescribed analgesic
    C. Assess blood pressure
    D. Notify the healthcare provider

Rationale:

Correct answer: C

Patients with spinal cord injury above T6 are at risk for autonomic dysreflexia (also known as autonomic hyperreflexia) which causes extreme hypertension that can lead to hemorrhage, seizure, stroke, or death. Symptoms include pounding headache, profuse sweating, nasal congestion, and bradycardia. Immediate BP assessment is priority. The nurse should be prepared to give IV push hydralazine or labetalol, and then check for fecal impaction to relieve the rectal stimulation. Other causes include bladder distention, unrelieved pain, or tactile stimulation.

A is incorrect because checking for fecal impaction is appropriate *after* blood pressure is assessed and treated.

B is incorrect because analgesic administration is not the priority action. It is critical that the nurse assess for autonomic dysreflexia, first.

D is incorrect because other actions must be taken before calling the healthcare provider. If the blood pressure is high (as one would expect, if this is autonomic dysreflexia), the nurse will immediately treat with IV antihypertensive medication before notifying the healthcare provider.

8. A patient is admitted for evaluation of the possibility of a spinal cord tumor. Which of the following assessment findings by the nurse warrants immediate action?

   A. New onset lower extremity weakness
   B. Chronic back pain 9/10
   C. Patient is crying and feels hopeless
   D. Patient is anxious about surgery, HR 110

Rationale:

Correct answer: A

Spinal cord tumors, or neoplasms, can arise from spinal cord cells or from metastasis of another tumor. Lower extremity weakness with new onset indicates compression of the spinal cord, which requires emergency medical and surgical intervention to prevent permanent loss of function. Intravenous corticosteroids can be given immediately to reduce the inflammation until the patient can be taken to the OR for tumor removal or decompression.

B is incorrect because chronic severe back pain is not as immediate of a concern as the new onset weakness. Non-mechanical back pain (pain that occurs without movement) is the most common symptom with a neoplastic spinal cord tumor.

C is incorrect because crying and feeling hopeless are psychosocial issues that do not take priority over actual physical problems.

D is incorrect because anxiety about surgery is common, and tachycardia is expected with anxiety. This warrants further investigation, reassurance, and possibly anxiolytic medication, but is not the greatest priority.

9. The nurse is caring for a 40-year-old patient with a cauda equina spinal cord injury. When planning care for this patient, which intervention should the nurse include?

   A. Catheterize every 3-4 hours
   B. Assist with ambulation four times a day ·
   C. Administer oxybutynin
   D. Stabilize neck when repositioning

Rationale:

Correct answer: A

Cauda equina syndrome is caused most often by disc herniation which compresses nerve roots at the end of the spinal cord. These nerve roots are responsible for sending and receiving signals from the lower extremities and the organs of the pelvis. Cauda equina injury can lead to irreversible damage and loss of bowel and bladder function. A reflexic bladder results from cauda equina syndrome, so regular catheterization should be utilized. These patients are at higher risk for UTI related to urine retention and inability to fully empty the bladder.

B is incorrect because the patient with cauda equina syndrome is unable to walk.

C is incorrect because oxybutynin is an anticholinergic medication is given to reduce bladder spasm, but the bladder of the cauda equina patient will be flaccid and spasms are not common.

D is incorrect because the neck (cervical spine) is unaffected in a patient with injury at the level of the cauda equina, in the lumbar region of the back.

10. A neurological nurse has received the hand-off report on four patients. Which of the following patients should be assessed by the nurse first?

    A. Patient admitted with botulism having a difficult time swallowing
    B. Patient admitted with Bell's palsy and herpes vesicles in front of the ear
    C. Patient admitted with neurosyphilis, tabes dorsalis, and diminished deep tendon reflexes
    D. Patient who has an abscess from drug use requiring a tetanus immune globulin injection

Rationale:

Correct answer: A

Botulism is a food-borne bacterium that is potentially fatal. Initial symptoms are weakness, difficulty seeing, trouble speaking, and lethargy. This can quickly progress to affect the muscles involved with respiration and can impair gas exchange, so the patient is at risk for respiratory failure. The nurse's priority is to immediately assess for signs of respiratory distress.

B is incorrect because a viral disease such as herpes is a common cause of Bell's palsy and does not require immediate intervention. Bell's palsy is damage to the seventh cranial nerve resulting in inability to close the eye, decreased corneal reflex, increased lacrimation, speech difficulty, loss of taste, and inability to control one side of the face.

C is incorrect because neurosyphilis is the infection of the brain and/or spinal column by the disease syphilis. Tabes dorsalis (slow demyelination of dorsal column of the spinal cord) and diminished deep tendon reflexes are consistent with neurosyphilis and do not require immediate intervention.

D is incorrect because treating an abscess and giving a tetanus shot are not emergency interventions.

11. The nurse on the neurological unit is caring for patients. Which of the following clinical manifestations in the patient with a spinal cord tumor is the most important to notify the healthcare provider of?

A. Back pain worsened by coughing

B. Scoliosis with 13% curvature, RR 18, SpO$_2$ 96%

C. Sudden clumsiness of hands

D. Pain that spreads to the hips, legs and feet, and is worse at night

Rationale:

Correct answer: C

A spinal cord tumor is an abnormal mass of tissue within or surrounding the spinal column. Primary tumors originate in the spine, and secondary tumors are metastatic from cancer spreading from another site in the body. Any sudden decrease in motor control, bowel, or bladder function is an indication of spinal cord compression which is an emergency that must be evaluated immediately. Untreated spinal cord compression can lead to permanent paralysis or even death.

A is incorrect because back pain is the most common presentation with spinal tumor. Pain that worsens with movement requires further assessment but is not an emergency.

B is incorrect because a tumor near the spine can cause an abnormal curvature, so this is somewhat expected. (The pulse ox and respiratory rate indicate the patient is *not* exhibiting respiratory compromise from a tumor pressing on the lungs, so this is not the greatest concern.)

D is incorrect because pain associated with a spinal tumor often is worse at night and can spread to other parts of the body.

12. The nurse is caring for an adult male patient with spinal cord injury. The patient is worried he will no longer be able to be intimate with his wife. What is the best response by the nurse?

A. "Erections as the result of reflex are common, but you may not be able to orgasm."

B. "Sildenafil is commonly used after spinal cord injury."

C. "There are many options for maintaining sexuality after a spinal cord injury."

D. "Vacuum suction devices, prostheses, and penile injections are options."

Rationale:

Correct answer: C

205

Spinal cord injury is damage that occurs from trauma that affects strength and sensation as well as body function below where the injury occurs. Sexuality is changed after spinal cord injury, but options are available for sexuality and fertility.

A is incorrect because reflex erections and ability to orgasm are dependent upon level and degree of injury.

B is incorrect because sildenafil need and effectiveness is dependent upon level and degree of injury. The nurse should be cautious about giving false reassurance and should attempt therapeutic communication and patient education about non-pharmacologic measures first.

D is incorrect because vacuum suction, prostheses, and injection need are dependent upon level and degree of injury.

13. The nurse is teaching at the community health center about how to prevent lower back injuries and pain. Which of the following instructions is most important to be included by the nurse?

    A. "Participation in exercise can strengthen muscles."
    B. "Purchase an adjustable firmness mattress."
    C. "Wear flats instead of heels for work."
    D. "Maintain your weight within 20% of ideal body weight."

Rationale:

Correct answer: A

Lower back pain can be caused by disc herniation, injury, and poor lifting techniques. One of the greatest ways to reduce lower back injuries and prevent back pain is to exercise regularly and increase core strength. Proper lifting techniques should also be taught, and quitting smoking should be encouraged.

B is incorrect because use of an adjustable mattress has not been medically proven to prevent or reduce lower back pain. The nurse should provide education that is relevant and realistic for patients to incorporate into their lifestyle. Purchase of new furniture items for the home are not covered by insurance plans, and patients are less likely to follow this advice than simpler instructions for lifestyle modification.

C is incorrect because wearing flats instead of heels *can* prevent lower back pain, but participation in regular exercise is more important. Exercise applies to patients of all populations, while high-heeled shoes applies only to women.

D is incorrect because maintaining healthy weight can reduce many complications but is not as directly related to lower back health as regular exercise.

14. A patient who experienced an injury at work is in the clinic with low back pain. Which instructions does the nurse include when planning care?

    A. "Perform back extension exercise by laying prone and lifting the arms and legs off the floor at the same time, hold for five seconds, then release, and repeat."
    B. "While lying flat on the floor on your back, perform leg lifts by lifting both legs straight towards the ceiling at the same time, hold for five seconds, then lower, and repeat."
    C. "Apply a heating pad to the lower back for 20 minutes, four times per day."
    D. "Avoid warm showers and baths."

Rationale:

Correct answer: C

Lower back pain can be caused by disc herniation, injury, and poor lifting techniques. Use of a heating pad will increase blood flow and promote healing of the injured nerves. Massage and stretching may also be helpful.

A is incorrect because this outdated exercise actually places a lot of compression on the lumbar vertebrae. Instead, the patient should lie prone and lift the right arm and left leg at the same time, then reverse.

B is incorrect because this method of leg lift places additional compression on the lumbar vertebrae. The exercise should be performed by bending one knee toward the chest, and then lifting the other leg straight towards the ceiling, then lower, and reverse.

D is incorrect because avoiding warm showers and baths is not necessary. Often, a warm shower or bath will actually help alleviate back pain.

15. A patient is admitted to the surgical unit after a discectomy six hours ago. When assessing the patient, which finding by the nurse should be addressed first?

A. Sleepy but awakens to voice

B. Dry, cracked oral mucosa

C. Pain in the lower back

D. Bladder palpated above the pubis

Rationale:

Correct answer: D

Discectomy is surgical removal of a displaced or herniated disc or disc material that is pressing on a nerve or the cord. Postoperative nursing care includes neurovascular observations, vital signs, pain assessment, patient-controlled-analgesia (PCA) management, I/O, and surgical wound observation. If the bladder can be palpated above the pubis, this indicates distention, which can signify sacral spinal nerve damage. This should be addressed first.

A is incorrect because drowsiness is common and expected after anesthesia. The post-op patient who awakes to voice is not a complication.

B is incorrect because dry, cracked oral mucosa is a sign of dehydration, which needs to be addressed, but is not as high priority as bladder distension.

C is incorrect because lower back pain is expected after a discectomy procedure. The patient will likely be on a PCA machine and may need further education about how to use the PCA. The nurse should assess dosage, usage and demand, and consider the need to change the PCA settings.

16. The nurse works at the community health center assessing clients at risk for lower back pain. Which of the following clients is at the greatest risk?

    A. 26-year-old female, smokes one pack of cigarettes a week, history of surgery for scoliosis at age 11

    B. 31-year-old female with Crohn's disease, takes prednisone daily

    C. 46-year-old male diagnosed with osteoarthritis

    D. 55-year-old female using a walker, chronic cough related to COPD

Rationale:

Correct answer: C

The 46-year-old male with osteoarthritis (OA) has three risk factors for lower back pain: age, gender, and OA.

Non-modifiable risks for lower back pain include, family history of back pain, male gender, middle-aged (45-65) or older, personal history of back injury, history of spinal surgery, osteoarthritis, depression, use of corticosteroids, and chronic coughing. Modifiable risk factors include sedentary lifestyle, smoking, excess body weight, and poor posture.

A is incorrect because the patient has two risk factors: smoking and history of back surgery.

B is incorrect because this patient has one risk factor: daily use of a corticosteroid medication.

D is incorrect because the patient has two risk factors: age and chronic cough.

17. A patient is admitted the surgical floor with a level T5 spinal cord injury. Their blood pressure is 180/90 mm Hg, and the patient appears flushed and states their vision is blurry. What is the first action the nurse should take?

   A. Place a nasal cannula with oxygen at 4L/min
   B. Place patient supine
   C. Palpate bladder for distention
   D. Administer beta blocker via IV

Rationale:

Correct answer: D

Autonomic dysreflexia (also known as autonomic hyperreflexia) is a rare complication that can occur in patients with spinal cord injury above T6. This emergency condition causes extremely high blood pressure, which can lead to other detrimental effects, even death. Other symptoms include pounding headache, profuse sweating, nasal congestion, and bradycardia. Immediate reduction of BP is the priority. Beta-blockers and hydralazine are the IV drugs of choice in this situation.

A is incorrect because autonomic dysreflexia is a circulatory problem, not an airway/breathing problem. Additional oxygen is not a priority. The nurse's greatest focus should be on lowering the blood pressure.

B is incorrect because placing the patient supine will worsen hypertension associated with autonomic dysreflexia. The best position is having the head of the bed elevated.

C is incorrect because lowering the blood pressure is the greatest priority. After the beta blocker is administered, the nurse can then investigate the stimulus, which is likely a full bladder or an impacted bowel.

18. A patient is brought to the emergency department with a cervical spinal cord injury. What is the first action the nurse should take?

    A. Level of consciousness assessment
    B. Vital signs
    C. Oxygen therapy
    D. Respiratory status evaluation

Rationale:

Correct answer: D

Patients with cervical spinal cord injury are at risk for respiratory impairment, due to decreased sensation and motor function of the muscles and organs of the upper chest. Assessing respiratory compromise and early intervention are the biggest priorities. This patient will likely need to be orally intubated to meet breathing and gas exchange needs.

A is incorrect because level of consciousness should be assessed after respiratory status. Whether or not the LOC has decreased, if the patient is not oxygenating well independently, intubation will be needed immediately.

B is incorrect because vital signs should be assessed after respiratory status.

C is incorrect because oxygen therapy may need to be initiated, but respiratory status must be evaluated first. If the patient does not have the ability to move the respiratory muscles involved in inspiration and expiration, applying oxygen will not be sufficient.

19. A patient with a lower motor neuron lesion desires bladder control. When the nurse teaches this patient, which statement should be included?

    A. "Stroking the inner aspect of the thigh will initiate voiding."
    B. "Let's review sterile technique for intermittent catheterization."
    C. "When your bladder is full, use digital anal stimulation."
    D. "Stimulate urine flow by tightening abdominal muscles."

Rationale:

Correct answer: D

Lower motor neuron lesions affect nerve fibers that innervate muscles and causes flaccid bladder paralysis. The Valsalva maneuver, or tightening abdominal muscles, can initiate urine elimination in these patients.

A is incorrect because stroking the inner thigh is used to stimulate urination in upper motor neuron dysfunction.

B is incorrect because intermittent catheterization is clean, not sterile, and it does not initiate voiding or help with bladder control. Catheterization is an option for patients who do not have the desire to void on their own. If the patient expresses that desire, catheterization technique should be taught by the nurse.

C is incorrect because digital anal stimulation will not initiate voiding or help with bladder control. Digital stimulation may be required as a part of a bowel program for paralyzed patients who do not have sensation in the rectum.

20. The nurse cares for a 39-year-old male patient who suffered a fall from a tree-stand while hunting. The patient now has paraplegia and is scheduled to participate in a physical therapy rehabilitation program. When the patient tells the nurse, "I don't understand the need for rehabilitation because my legs will never work again," what is the best response by the nurse?

    A. "You have the right to choose whether you want to participate in a rehabilitation program."
    B. "Rehabilitation has helped many young sportsmen with the same type of injury. Give it a chance."
    C. "Rehabilitation can help you learn how to maintain functional ability and prevent further disability."
    D. "Those who are in rehabilitation are the first patients to benefit from new discoveries regarding paraplegia management."

Rationale:

Correct answer: C

Paraplegia is motor and/or sensory impairment that affects the lower extremities. Although return of function and sensation is not common, patients with paraplegia require rehabilitation to prevent disability, maintain functional ability, and preserve their independence with activities of daily living. Rehabilitation programs can also offer a valuable source of peer support from others who have undergone similar injuries.

A is incorrect because it does not provide information that will help the patient. While it *is* the patient's legal right to refuse treatment, the nurse should use communication strategies that are therapeutic and provide information to help the patient make the decision that will benefit them the most. Discussion of refusal of care is a last resort, after the patient has been given the information about the benefits of rehabilitation therapy.

B is incorrect because this response uses casual language which does not answer the patient's question, and it focuses on *other* patients. Therapeutic communication involves the nurse staying focused on the patient, providing facts, acknowledging the patient's feelings, and promoting quality of life.

D is incorrect because participating in rehabilitation does not necessarily mean the patient will have early benefit from new research and techniques for paraplegia management and treatment.

21. A patient has been in the hospital for 27 days after a debilitating spinal cord injury. The nurse is providing discharge teaching. Which of the following patient statements demonstrates they understand how to prevent respiratory problems after discharge?

    A. "I should use the incentive spirometer 10 times every hour while awake."
    B. "I should drink fluids that have been thinned, for prevention of choking."
    C. "Cough medicine should be taken for prevention of excessive coughing."
    D. "I'll lay on my right side after eating to prevent aspiration."

Rationale:

Correct answer: A

Spinal cord injury can cause lifelong impairment in sensation and function below the level of the injury. Weakening of intercostal muscles and accessory breathing muscles used for inspiration and expiration places the patient at increased risk for atelectasis and stasis pneumonia. It is critical that the patient learns technique for use of the incentive spirometer and understands the need for the frequency to keep their lungs expanded fully and prevent atelectasis as a part of their regular routine.

B is incorrect because thick liquids are generally easier to swallow. Water, coffee, milk, soda, juice, and broth are thin liquids that should be avoided or used with caution.

C is incorrect because the patient needs to cough and clear secretions routinely. Cough suppressants can inhibit the ability of the lungs to fully clear.

D is incorrect because the patient should be in high Fowler's position (sitting upright) for prevention of aspiration. Lying on the right side *does* promote gastric emptying into the duodenum, but High Fowler's position, or sitting upright slightly turned towards the right side, are better position options after meal consumption.

22. A patient is admitted to the emergency department with acute exacerbation of multiple sclerosis (MS). Which of the following prescribed medications should be prepared for administration by the nurse?

   A. Baclofen
   B. Interferon beta-1b
   C. Tetracycline
   D. Methylprednisolone

Rationale:

Correct answer: D

Multiple sclerosis (MS) is a disease of demyelination of the nerve cells, brain, and spinal cord leading to vision, motor, and sensation changes. The etiology of MS is unclear. Late complications of MS include bowel changes and cognitive impairment, but the mentation and intellect generally remain intact. It is a progressive disease that can exacerbate, leading to permanent neurological symptoms after an attack. Symptoms experienced during an attack may include muscular incoordination, ataxia, spasticity, nystagmus, chewing and swallowing difficulties, and impaired speech. Methylprednisolone is the best medication to administer for acute exacerbations.

A is incorrect because baclofen is given specifically to decrease muscle spasticity associated with MS but is not necessarily the priority medication in an exacerbation.

B is incorrect because interferon beta-1b is given routinely for treatment and control of MS, to decrease specific symptoms, and to slow the progression of the disease. This is not a medication given for an acute exacerbation.

C is incorrect because tetracycline is contraindicated in MS because it can increase muscle weakness.

23. A patient with multiple sclerosis is given fingolimod, as ordered, by the nurse. Which adverse effect should the nurse monitor for?

    A. Peripheral edema
    B. Black, tarry stools
    C. Bradycardia
    D. Nausea and vomiting

Rationale:

Correct answer: C

Multiple sclerosis (MS) is a disease in which nerve cells become demyelinated in the brain and spinal cord. Symptoms include vision, motor and sensation changes, progressing to bowel changes, and cognitive impairment, but the mentation and intellect generally remain intact. Fingolimod is an immune-omodulating drug that sequesters lymphocytes in lymph nodes, preventing them from contributing to an auto-immune reaction. Bradycardia can occur within six hours of administration, so heart rate monitoring is a nursing priority. Other more common side effects include headache, head cold, and fatigue.

A is incorrect because peripheral edema is not an adverse effect of fingolimod. (SSRIs, hormonal antineoplastic agents, calcium channel blockers, thiazide diuretics and metformin can all cause peripheral edema.)

B is incorrect because black, tarry stools are indicative of GI bleeding, which is not an adverse effect of fingolimod. (Black, tarry stools can result from gastric ulcer, typhoid fever, blood clotting disorder, indomethacin use, iron supplementation, or Crohn's disease.)

D is incorrect because nausea and vomiting are common side effects to many drugs but not specific to fingolimod.

24. A patient with multiple sclerosis is learning about recently prescribed cyclophosphamide and methylprednisolone. When providing discharge instructions, which statement should be included by the nurse?

    A. "Warm baths can be taken for muscle relaxation."
    B. "Avoid large crowds and sick people."
    C. "Your gait will weaken if you rely on a walker."
    D. "Be sure to take your medications when you have symptoms."

Rationale:

Correct answer: B

Multiple sclerosis (MS) is a disease in which nerve cells become demyelinated in the brain and spinal cord. Symptoms include vision, motor, and sensation changes, progressing to bowel changes and cognitive impairment, but the mentation and intellect generally remain intact. MS is a progressive disease that can exacerbate, leading to permanent neurological symptoms after an attack. Cyclophosphamide and methylprednisolone are immunosuppressive drugs, so they will lessen the body's ability to fight infection. People who have upper respiratory illness are often found in large crowds, so these should be avoided to prevent contraction of infection.

A is incorrect because a warm bath will exacerbate symptoms. For many MS patients, even slight elevations in body temperatures can cause neurological changes. In fact: for many years, the "Hot Bath Test" was used to diagnose MS. A person suspected of having MS was immersed in a hot tub of water. The appearance of neurologic symptoms or their worsening was taken as evidence the person had MS.

C is incorrect because a walker may be needed for safety when ambulating. The nurse is responsible for teaching the MS patient how to use a walker for safe ambulation and how to also maximize gait and muscle strength. The nurse may also consult with physical therapy and occupational therapy for assistance with this type of patient education, when available.

D is incorrect because MS medications should be taken daily at regular intervals, as scheduled, not just when the patient is symptomatic.

25. A nurse working on the neurological unit is caring for four patients. Which order for a patient would require the nurse to confirm informed consent is completed before the test or procedure?

A. Sensation measurement with pinprick method

B. Computed tomography of cranial vault

C. Lumbar puncture with cerebrospinal fluid sampling

D. Venipuncture for venous blood analysis of autoantibodies

Rationale:

Correct answer: C

Invasive procedures require informed consent. Lumbar puncture is an invasive procedure in which a needle is inserted into the subarachnoid space to obtain a CSF specimen, inject dye, inject medications, or relieve pressure. This procedure is done either at the bedside or in a treatment room. Because it is invasive and has potentially serious complications, such as headache, decreased ICP, and infection, this procedure requires signed informed consent. The healthcare provider must explain the procedure and obtain the patient's signature, and the nurse signs as a witness.

A is incorrect because sensation measurement with pinprick measurement is not invasive and requires only verbal consent.

B is incorrect because computed tomography is not invasive and generally does not require signed informed consent. (In some facilities, if the CT is to be done with contrast injected or swallowed, informed consent may be necessary due to the increased risks from the contrast dye.)

D is incorrect because venipuncture only requires verbal consent.

26. A patient is scheduled for magnetic resonance imaging (MRI) without contrast. Which of the following actions should be implemented by the nurse before the test?

    A. NPO status for eight hours

    B. Withhold daily medications until after MRI

    C. Administer morphine for prevention of claustrophobia

    D. Place patient in gown with cloth ties

Rationale:

Correct answer: D

MRI has a magnetic field, and metal objects are a hazard around the MRI. A gown with cloth ties (as opposed to metal snaps) should be placed on the patient to prevent injury to the patient. All metal objects and jewelry must be removed.

A is incorrect because NPO status is unnecessary for MRI. NPO is required for procedures that require sedation and for many GI procedures which require the stomach and GI tract to be empty for the test. Note: MRI is not routinely done with sedation, although sedation may be necessary for MRI in children or patients who are unable to lie still for the duration of the test.

B is incorrect because withholding daily medications is unnecessary for MRI without contrast.

C is incorrect because morphine will not prevent claustrophobia in MRI. Lorazepam is a short-term anxiolytic medication that is most commonly used as a pre-medication for those who are anxious or claustrophobic.

27. A patient with a spinal cord injury is admitted to the neurological unit. Which of the following interdisciplinary team members would the nurse consult regarding activities of daily living?

    A. Social worker
    B. Physical therapist
    C. Occupational therapist
    D. Case manager

Rationale:

Correct answer: C

Spinal cord injury is damage that occurs from trauma that affects strength and sensation as well as body function below where the injury occurred. An occupational therapist (OT) will evaluate physical and environmental barriers in the home and provide training in the use of low- and high-tech assistive and adaptive technology equipment. The nurse collaborates with the OT in instructing caregivers and family members regarding transfer, feeding, dressing, positioning, bathing, and skin care. The OT will also help modify activities and environments where needed and evaluate and recommend wheelchair seating and positioning systems to optimize function, mobility, and engagement in the community.

A is incorrect because the social worker does not consult for activities of daily living. The role of the social worker in spinal cord injury is to provide initial crisis intervention. They also act as a liaison between the medical team and the family, provide information, allow the family to vent feelings and concerns, and provide counseling to help increase the patient's self-esteem, self-worth and self-efficacy. Additionally, the social worker will identify resources and referrals to agencies that can help with a variety of concerns and provide continual counseling throughout the process of adjustment to address anxiety, re-entry into social/work environments, and relationship/caregiver issues.

B is incorrect because the physical therapist (PT) does not consult for activities of daily living. The most common PT activities with spinal cord injury patients involve muscle strengthening exercises, stretching, transfer training, wheelchair mobility training, and gait training.

D is incorrect because the case manager does not consult for activities of daily living. The case manager is responsible for coordination of care with the multidisciplinary team. Other duties include overseeing follow-up consultations and facilitating communication between care providers.

28. A patient diagnosed with amyotrophic lateral sclerosis (ALS) tells the nurse they do not wish to be intubated and placed on mechanical ventilation. What is the best response by the nurse?

   A. "This should be discussed with your healthcare provider."
   B. "Why don't you want to be on the breathing machine?"
   C. "Incentive spirometer use every hour will delay need for being placed on the ventilator."
   D. "What would you prefer we do if you experience difficulty with breathing?"

Rationale:

Correct answer: D

ALS (Lou Gehrig's Disease) is a progressive, degenerative disease involving the lower motor neurons of the spinal cord and cerebral cortex. The voluntary motor system is primarily involved. ALS is characterized by weakness that sets in progressively, wasting of muscles, and spasticity that leads to paralysis. When breathing muscles become involved, the patient must have an advance directive that indicates the patient's wishes regarding breathing assistance. Respiratory insufficiency is the usual cause of death for patients with ALS.

A is incorrect because the statement does not promote the nurse-patient relationship. While it *is* important to discuss the issue with the healthcare provider, it is more therapeutic and patient-centered for the nurse to address the patient's wishes and help explain alternatives to mechanical ventilation.

B is incorrect because it is non-therapeutic to ask a patient "why?" It *is* important to determine the patient's concerns, but the nurse should do so without asking "why?" A better statement would be "What are your concerns about the mechanical ventilation?"

C is incorrect because the statement does not address patient needs. It *is* a true statement, and it provides factual information, but it doesn't address the patient's stated concern.

29. A patient is in the clinic with chronic back pain and the healthcare provider prescribes ziconotide. While assessing the patient's health history, which question should the nurse ask?

    A. "Do you take nonsteroidal anti-inflammatory drugs?"
    B. "Is there a mental health disorder present?"
    C. "Can you swallow medications?"
    D. "Do you use illegal drugs or smoke cigarettes?"

Rationale:

Correct answer: B

Ziconotide is an analgesic agent (atypical) used for amelioration of chronic and severe pain. Ziconotide can rarely cause new or worsening depression, paranoia but should not be taken by patients who have a history of psychosis, clinical depression, schizophrenia, or bipolar disorder.

A is incorrect because taking nonsteroidal anti-inflammatory drugs is not a contraindication for ziconotide. NSAIDs have a different mechanism of action and can be used in conjunction with ziconotide for pain relief.

C is incorrect because ability to swallow medications is not a contraindication for ziconotide. This medication is only approved for use when injected intrathecally, directly into the cerebrospinal fluid.

D is incorrect because use of illegal drugs or smoking cigarettes is not a direct contraindication for ziconotide. (However, this is an appropriate general question to ask *any* patient because smoking and illegal drug use should be discouraged and the patient should be educated about associated health risks with these habits.)

30. A 52-year-old mountain climber is admitted to the emergency room with confusion and bizarre behavior. After oxygen is administered, which priority intervention should be implemented by the nurse?

    A. Administration of dexamethasone
    B. Complete mini-mental state examination (MMSE)
    C. Prepare for brain computed tomography
    D. Request psychiatric consult

Rationale:

Correct answer: A

This patient has signs of high altitude cerebral edema (HACE) and acute mountain sickness (AMS). Effects vary for each individual, but the most classic initial symptoms include headache, insomnia, anorexia, nausea, and dizziness. Dexamethasone is a glucocorticoid steroid which will reduce cerebral edema due to its anti-inflammatory effects on the central nervous system.

B is incorrect because completing a mini-mental state examination (MMSE) will not diagnose or treat HACE or AMS. The MMSE is a structured assessment of a patient's behavioral and cognitive function and is used to differentiate types of dementias.

C is incorrect because computed tomography of the brain may help in diagnosing HACE, but dexamethasone should be given first to reduce brain swelling.

D is incorrect because a psychiatric consult is not required.

31. A patient who experienced damage to the left temporal lobe of the brain will be educated by the nurse. When teaching the patient about new medications, which action should be taken by the nurse?

    A. Assist the patient in identifying medications by color
    B. Give the patient large print written materials

C. Sit on patient's right side and use written materials for medication education

D. Use a white board for the patient to write questions

Rationale:

Correct answer: C

The auditory center is located in the temporal lobe. Damage to the left temporal lobe will affect sound interpretation and hearing is impaired on the left side. The nurse needs to sit on the right side and speak into the patient's right ear. Left temporal lobe damage can also disturb recognition of words and impaired memory for verbal material, so written materials are best to help the patient retain the information.

A is incorrect because identifying medications by color will not address damage to the left temporal lobe. Many medications may be similarly colored, so if a patient has the inability to read the labels on the prescription bottles, it is best to help teach them how to identify their meds by color, shape, *and* size.

B is incorrect because large print is not necessary, as the vision is not impaired with left temporal lobe injury. Also, simply giving the patient written materials is not enough; the nurse must also actively explain the information.

D is incorrect because use of a white board will not address damage to the left temporal lobe. The patient with left temporal lobe damage will still be able to talk. *Right* temporal damage can cause a loss of inhibition of talking.

32. A patient's recent memory is tested by the nurse. Which statement by the patient demonstrates that the patient's recent memory is unimpaired?

    A. "The young girl wearing a shroud sleeps on clouds."
    B. "I was born April 4, 1968, at Johnson Community Hospital."
    C. "Apple, pencil, and table are what you just stated."
    D. "I ate cereal with a banana and apple juice for breakfast."

Rationale:

Correct answer: D

Recent memory (also called short-term memory or working memory) is best tested by asking about verifiable events, including what was consumed for breakfast.

A is incorrect because making up a rhyme tests a higher level of cognition. Other ways to test higher cognition include multiple choice questions, problem-solving, and short essay questions.

B is incorrect because asking about personal historical events is a test of remote memory, not recent memory. Remote memory involves memory of events that may have happened years ago.

C is incorrect because repeating words assesses immediate memory, which is the ability to remember a small amount of information over a few seconds.

33. A patient displays a positive Romberg's sign with their eyes closed, but not open, when tested by the nurse. Which condition is associated with the nurse's finding?

    A. Difficulty with proprioception
    B. Peripheral motor disorder
    C. Impaired cerebellar function
    D. Positive pronator drift

Rationale:

Correct answer: A

Romberg's test is a neurological assessment for body position and balance. The nurse asks the patient to stand with feet together and eyes opened for a minute. Then, the nurse assesses the patient for another minute with the eyes closed. Romberg's test is positive if the patient sways or falls when the eyes are closed. This indicates a proprioception disorder which is compensated by vision. Proprioception disorder results from neuropathy or posterior vertebral column disease.

B is incorrect because peripheral motor disorder would not cause a positive Romberg's sign. Nerve conduction studies are used to diagnose peripheral motor disorder.

C is incorrect because Romberg's test is not used to diagnose cerebellar disease. Finger-to-nose and finger-to-finger testing, heel-to-shin testing, and gait assessment are some tests used to assess cerebellar damage.

D is incorrect because positive pronator drift would not cause a positive Romberg's sign. Pronator drift is a sign of upper motor neuron lesion.

34. The patient asks the nurse why deep breaths are requested during electroencephalography (EEG). What is the best response by the nurse?

   A. "Hyperventilation will cause cerebral artery dilation, which leads to decreased electoral brain activity."
   B. "Deep breathing helps with relaxation and a better waveform with electroencephalography."
   C. "Hyperventilation will cause cerebral vasoconstriction and increased likelihood of a seizure."
   D. "Deep breathing blows off carbon dioxide and decreases pressure in the intracranial cavity."

Rationale:

Correct answer: C

Electroencephalography (EEG) is performed to record the electrical activity in the brain. The procedure is done by an EEG technician in a quiet room. The patient may be asked to hyperventilate (20-30 deep breaths per minute for three to four minutes), which causes cerebral vasoconstriction and alkalosis. This can stimulate seizure activity (which is what the EEG is monitoring for). It is also common to expose the patient to bright, flashing lights prior to the EEG, as this can cause seizure activity as well.

A is incorrect because the statement is inaccurate.

B is incorrect because the statement is inaccurate. Deep breathing *may* be used for relaxation in some patients, but this is not the purpose related to EEG testing.

D is incorrect because although deep breathing *does* reduce CO_2, the purpose during EEG is not to decrease ICP. The purpose is to stimulate seizure activity.

35. A patient recovering from cerebral angiography via right femoral artery is assessed by the nurse. Which assessment should be completed by the nurse?

   A. Palpate lower extremity pulses bilaterally
   B. Assess for orthostatic hypotension
   C. Perform fundoscopic examination
   D. Assess gag reflex before meals

Rationale:

Correct answer: A

The brachial or femoral artery is accessed with a catheter to perform cerebral angiography. Following the procedure, the affected extremity is immobilized. Adequate circulation is checked by assessing skin color and temperature, pulses, and capillary refill. Decrease in circulation should be reported to the healthcare provider immediately.

B is incorrect because orthostatic blood pressure assessment requires the BP to be monitored in several positions. Post-femoral-angiography, the patient must remain on bedrest with the affected leg extended and the head-of bed flat.

C is incorrect because fundoscopic examination is unaffected by cerebral angiography. Fundoscopic examination is ophthalmic examination of the fundus of the eye, used to assess retinal damages from hypertension.

D is incorrect because assessing gag reflex before meals is not routine for post-angiography patients.

36. A patient has deteriorating neurologic function. When the patient tells the nurse they are worried about being able to care for their young children, what is the best response by the nurse?

    A. "Child care is priority. You need to ask for help, even though you may not want to."
    B. "There are community resources to help with household tasks so you can care for your children."
    C. "You seem to be distressed. Can I have the psychologist speak to you about adjustment to your condition?"
    D. "Tell me more about what you are worried about so I can see what we can do to make adjustments."

Rationale:

Correct answer: D

The nurse needs to find out specifically what the patient is concerned about regarding role changes and neurologic status before providing information.

A is incorrect because the nurse should remain focused on the patient's concerns without being blunt and non-therapeutic.

B is incorrect because community resources are possibly available, but appropriateness has not been determined.

C is incorrect because the nurse needs to find out what the concerns are before consulting with the psychologist. This answer "passes the buck" to another member of the healthcare team. The nurse should remain focused on strengthening the nurse-patient relationship.

37. The nurse is assessing pain discrimination on a 64-year-old patient. With eyes closed, the patient correctly identifies a sharp sensation on the right hand when touched with a pin. What is the next action the nurse should take?

    A. Repeat the assessment on the left hand
    B. Notify the healthcare provider with results
    C. Ask about current medications
    D. Continue with the feet next

Rationale:

Correct answer: A

The pain discrimination assessment is performed to test sensory receptors and identify if a specific side of the brain has been affected by disease or damage. When testing is started on the right hand and correctly identified by the patient, the assessment is continued with the left hand to assess for equality of findings.

B is incorrect because the patient correctly identified the sharp sensation which does not warrant notification of the healthcare provider. Since this is an expected finding, it should be documented in the patient's chart. (The healthcare provider is notified when *unexpected* findings are present.)

C is incorrect because current medications are unnecessary to assess with this finding.

D is incorrect because the left hand is assessed before continuing with the lower extremities.

38. The nurse is caring for a patient with cranial nerve II impairment. Which statement should be included by the nurse when delegating care for this patient to the unlicensed assistive personnel (UAP)?

A. "Be sure to tell the patient where food is located on the tray."

B. "Make sure the patient is in high-Fowler's for meals."

C. "Ensure the patient's food is spread out on the tray so the patient can visualize the separate food items."

D. "Place the patient's fork in the left hand."

Rationale:

Correct answer: A

Cranial nerve II (the optic nerve) provides the central as well as peripheral vision. When this cranial nerve is impaired, the patient's normal vision will be impaired. It is appropriate for the UAP to tell the patient where food is located on the tray.

B is incorrect because semi-Fowler's (HOB 30-45 degrees) is appropriate for this patient during meals. High-Fowler's (sitting upright) is appropriate for a patient who is at risk for aspiration, such as a spinal cord injury patient.

C is incorrect because the patient with cranial nerve II impairment is unable to see.

D is incorrect because upper extremity coordination and muscle control will not be affected by cranial nerve II impairment, so the patient should be able to determine in which hand to hold the fork (dominant side).

39. A nurse caring for a patient with Guillain-Barre is learning the pathophysiology includes segmental demyelination. The nurse understands that this causes what?

A. Delayed impulses of afferent nerves, not efferent nerves

B. Affected muscle paralysis

C. Unilateral paresthesia

D. Nerve impulse transmission slowing

Rationale:

Correct answer: D

Guillain-Barre is a progressive, inflammatory autoimmune disorder which causes peripheral nerve root compression. The immune system attacks nerves, causing demyelination, which slows peripheral nerve impulse conduction and can leads to paralysis, over time. Acute, rapidly progressing ascending sensory and motor deficit can stop at any point along the CNS, or progress to the spinal cord.

A is incorrect because Guillain-Barre causes delayed impulses of both afferent and efferent nerves. Afferent nerves bring signals from the body to the central nervous system (sensation). Efferent nerves send signals from the CNS to the rest of the body (muscle control).

B is incorrect because Guillain-Barre does not cause muscle paralysis in any specific muscle and is not associated with a single affected muscle. The muscle weakness and decreased sensation (or numbness, tingling) generally are experienced bilaterally, more in the lower extremities than in the upper extremities.

C is incorrect because Guillain-Barre causes bilateral symptoms.

NCLEX-RN – MED-SURG: MUSCULOSKELETAL – 40 QUESTIONS

1. An older adult community group is learning about healthy aging. What is the best recommendation the nurse can make for prevention of osteoarthritis (OA)?

   A. Contact sports should be avoided
   B. Increase calcium intake
   C. Lose weight if necessary
   D. Perform weight-bearing exercises

   Rationale:

   Correct answer: C

   Osteoarthritis, or degenerative joint disease, is the breakdown of cartilage in joints that leads to stiffness, pain, and usually affects the wrists, neck, knees, hips, hands, or back. Risk for OA increases with age. Maintaining ideal body weight can prevent osteoarthritis by decreasing the weight on joints that leads to osteoarthritis.

   A is incorrect because obesity is a more significant contributor to OA than contact sports. Contact sports do not need to be avoided, but if repetitive sports activities cause pain, the patient should consider switching activities. Other repetitive activities may include occupations such as carpet installation, manufacturing assembly line work, construction work, and farming.

   B is incorrect because calcium intake is important for preventing osteoporosis.

   D is incorrect because weight-bearing exercise is important for preventing osteoporosis.

2. A family clinic nurse is educating a client who was recently diagnosed with osteoarthritis (OA). Which medications for treating OA does the nurse primarily plan teaching around?

A. Acetaminophen

B. Cyclobenzaprine hydrochloride

C. Hyaluronate

D. Cyclosporine

Rationale:

Correct answer: A

Osteoarthritis, or degenerative joint disease, is the breakdown of cartilage in joints that leads to stiffness, pain, and usually affects the wrists, neck, knees, hips, hands, or back. The first line medication for osteoarthritis pain is acetaminophen, which rarely causes side effects.

B is incorrect because cyclobenzaprine is appropriate for OA but is given for muscle spasms, not pain. Side effects include dizziness, fatigue, and dry mouth.

C is incorrect because hyaluronate is appropriate for OA but is a joint fluid synthetic injection. Hyaluronate is used to increase effectiveness of fluid within a joint to act as a lubricant and a shock absorber. This medication is not typically prescribed unless other pain treatment options fail.

D is incorrect because cyclosporine is given to transplant patients to prevent organ rejection.

3. A client with diabetes is assessed in the family practice clinic by the nurse. The client has a history of osteoarthritis (OA), and blood glucose readings have been higher than usual. What is the most appropriate question by the nurse?

    A. "Do you take chondroitin?"

    B. "Are you taking glucosamine supplements?"

    C. "How much do you exercise each week?"

    D. "You're taking diabetic medication, correct?"

Rationale:

Correct answer: B

Osteoarthritis, or degenerative joint disease, is the breakdown of cartilage in joints that leads to stiffness, pain, and usually affects the wrists, neck, knees, hips, hands, or back.

Glucosamine is sometimes taken for OA in order to promote collagen synthesis. Glucosamine can impede insulin secretion and raise blood sugar levels, so the nurse should ask the patient whether it is being used. Glucosamine can also cause nausea, heartburn, and diarrhea.

A is incorrect because the chondroitin does not impact blood sugar. Chondroitin is often with glucosamine to aide in collagen synthesis for musculoskeletal problems, such as OA. Chondroitin can potentiate the effectiveness of anticoagulants.

C is incorrect because asking about exercise is appropriate but will not elicit specific information related to the OA and increased blood glucose.

D is incorrect because asking the patient about taking diabetic medication in this manner is patronizing (treats the patient with kindness but portrays a feeling of superiority).

4. A 72-year-old patient is transferred to the medical-surgical unit to recover from total hip replacement. Upon assessment, the nurse finds the patient is restless and disoriented. What is the most important intervention to prevent injury?

   A. Mild sedation administration
   B. Maintain all siderails raised
   C. Restrain patient's hands
   D. Use abduction pillow

Rationale:

Correct answer: D

Total hip replacement is a surgical procedure performed to replace a joint damaged by osteoarthritis, fracture, or other causes. Older patients have a slower metabolism of anesthetics as well as pain medication, which could cause restlessness and confusion following surgery. The abduction pillow should be used at this time to prevent hip dislocation as the patient may be unable to follow directions and maintain proper body alignment post-op. The abduction pillow prevents the patient from getting into a position that can cause hip prosthesis dislocation (adduction, internal rotation.)

A is incorrect because sedation can worsen restlessness and disorientation. The nurse should avoid sedating a disoriented patient if at all possible.

B is incorrect because all siderails raised is considered a restraint and the nurse should attempt to provide for safety with least restrictive measures. The concern here is dislocation of hip prosthesis, not falling out of bed.

C is incorrect because restraining the patient's hands is unnecessary and even more restrictive than siderails raised. Restraining hands may increase risk for injury and will not keep the hip in proper alignment.

5. A 54-year-old female patient is admitted to the surgical unit for total knee replacement. The patient has a history of asthma. Which action is most important for perioperative staff to prevent surgical wound infection?

   A. Administer ordered preoperative antibiotic
   B. Assess white blood cell (WBC) count
   C. Instruct patient to take a shower the night before
   D. Monitor postoperative temperature

Rationale:

Correct answer: A

Preoperative antibiotics are administered within one hour of surgery to prevent infection of surgical wounds. Along with aseptic technique when caring for the incision afterwards, this is a very important component of infection prevention.

B is incorrect because monitoring white blood cell count will not prevent infection.

C is incorrect because a shower with antimicrobial soap is beneficial but not as effective as preoperative antibiotics.

D is incorrect because monitoring temperature may show an indication of infection but is not a preventative measure.

6. While assessing a patient recovering from total hip replacement, the nurse notes the leg with the replacement hip is shorter than the other and the patient is reporting pain 10/10. What is the best action by the nurse to perform while another nurse calls the surgeon?

   A. Assess bilateral neurovascular status
   B. Elevate the surgical leg and apply an ice pack

C. Administer pain medication

D. Attempt to place surgical leg in abduction

Rationale:

Correct answer: A

Total hip replacement is a surgical procedure performed to replace a joint damaged by osteoarthritis, fracture, along with several other causes. One leg shorter than the other and extreme pain is characteristic of hip dislocation, a complication that can occur with this surgery. Dislocation of the hip can lead to neurovascular compromise, so this should be assessed bilaterally for the lower extremities. Other complications after hip replacement include excessive wound drainage, thromboembolism, and infection.

B is incorrect because elevation of the leg is contraindicated if hip dislocation is suspected. Ice packs can be applied to reduce swelling and minimize pain, but assessing circulation is more important.

C is incorrect because pain medication should be administered, but neurovascular assessment should be performed first. Physical assessment needs take priority over pain treatment.

D is incorrect because abducting the leg is contraindicated when dislocation is suspected.

7. A patient recovering from total knee replacement has a continuous passive motion (CPM) device ordered. After the patient is returned to bed and the leg placed in the device, which action can be delegated to the unlicensed assistive personnel (UAP) by the nurse?

    A. Assess distal circulation

    B. Decrease range of motion settings if patient complains of pain

    C. Raise the bed's lower siderail on the patient's affected side

    D. Determine if the patient needs pain medication

Rationale:

Correct answer: C

Continuous passive motion (CPM) is utilized after joint surgery to keep the joint moving and prevent stiffness and maintain range of motion. The device slowly flexes and extends the knee. With the leg strapped in the CPM machine, the movement of the machine could cause it to shift and fall off of the bed, in turn injuring the patient's leg and new joint. The UAP should be instructed to raise the siderails to prevent the CPM machine from shifting off the bed. Another important nursing action is to protect skin from rubbing on the CPM frame by applying sheepskin padding between the skin and the frame.

A is incorrect because assessment of distal circulation is the nurse's responsibility.

B is incorrect because the CPM settings are only adjusted by the surgeon, physical therapist, or trained technician.

D is incorrect because it is not within the UAP's scope of practice to assess pain or offer pain medication.

8. A patient recovering from total right knee replacement has continuous right femoral nerve blockade. While assessing the patient, the nurse notes the pedal pulses are 2+/4+ bilaterally, skin is pale pink, warm, and dry, and the patient does not have the ability to point or flex the foot. What is the next action by the nurse?

   A. Document findings and continue to monitor
   B. Reassess pulses with a bedside Doppler
   C. Notify the surgeon or anesthesiologist immediately
   D. Palpate bladder or scan bladder with scanner

Rationale:

Correct answer: C

Continuous femoral nerve blockade is administered to prevent pain distal to the infusion, usually after surgery or joint replacement. With this blockade, the patient retains the ability to dorsiflex and plantarflex the affected foot, so if the patient is unable to do this, the surgeon or anesthesiologist should be notified immediately.

A is incorrect because patient care takes priority over documentation. Abnormal findings must be addressed before documentation is completed.

B is incorrect because a Doppler may be used to reassess pulses, but the most important action is to notify the healthcare provider.

D is incorrect because palpation of the bladder is unrelated to loss of neuromuscular function in the affected foot.

9. A patient is being discharged to short-term rehabilitation after total hip replacement procedure. Which is the most important action by the nurse?

   A. Administer pain medication prior to transport
   B. Answer last-minute questions by patient
   C. Provide directions to the rehabilitation facility to family
   D. Provide a verbal hand-off report to the facility

Rationale:

Correct answer: D

A hand-off report is a Joint Commission standard that must be performed for patient safety and prevention of errors. JCAHO recommends adequate time for successful hand-off, use of standardized procedure such as SBAR (situation, background, assessment, recommendation), and shared accountability during all points of transition.

A is incorrect because pain medication is important, but an accurate and complete hand-off report is greater priority.

B is incorrect because answering patient questions is important but not priority.

C is incorrect because directions to the facility can be given by another member of the care team; the nurse is specifically responsible for the hand-off report.

10. Which patient with rheumatoid arthritis (RA) should the nurse in the clinic assess first?

    A. Patient reporting jaw pain with eating
    B. Patient whose right wrist is red, hot, and swollen
    C. Patient who developed a swollen area behind the right knee
    D. Patient whose joint deformity is worse since the last exam

Rationale:

Correct answer: B

Rheumatoid arthritis (RA) is an autoimmune form of arthritis that affects wrists, small joints of the hands, knuckles, and other joints. It is characterized by swelling, pain, and decreased mobility of the joints. A joint that is red, hot, and swollen may be infected and needs to be assessed first.

A is incorrect because jaw pain is possibly due to RA but is not priority.

C is incorrect because swelling behind the knee is possibly due to RA but is not priority.

D is incorrect because joint deformity is possibly due to RA but is not priority. Progressive joint deformity is a characteristic of RA and is expected.

11. A patient with a history of rheumatoid arthritis (RA) is recovering from elective surgery on the postoperative unit. The patient is reporting pain in the neck since surgery. What is the first action the nurse should take?

   A. Assist the patient in changing positions
   B. Document findings in the patient's chart
   C. Encourage neck range of motion exercises
   D. Monitor respiratory status

Rationale:

Correct answer: D

Rheumatoid arthritis (RA) is a chronic, autoimmune form of arthritis that affects wrists, small joints of the hands, knuckles, and other joints. It is characterized by swelling, pain, and decreased mobility of the joints. The neck can be affected by RA and could lead to phrenic nerve compression, which can paralyze the diaphragm and compromise respiratory status. Permanent injury to the spinal cord can also occur. Respiratory status should be assessed, and the healthcare provider should be notified.

A is incorrect because changing positions may alleviate the pain but could also worsen the patient's condition.

B is incorrect because documentation is priority after patient care has been completed. The compromise to the neck and respiratory system must be addressed ahead of documentation.

C is incorrect because range of motion exercise could worsen the patient's condition.

12. The nurse cares for a female 49-year-old patient with rheumatoid arthritis (RA) and Sjogren's syndrome. Which is the most important action for the nurse to take?

A. Perform an abdominal assessment

B. Teach the patient to avoid nasal spray

C. Draw blood to test for renal function

D. Assess visual acuity

Rationale:

Correct answer: D

Sjogren's syndrome is an immune system disorder that commonly occurs with RA and lupus and leads to dry mouth and eyes, as well as vaginal dryness. The nurse must assess visual acuity as disturbances in vision may occur with Sjogren's syndrome. This syndrome mostly affects people over the age of 40 and is more common in women.

A is incorrect because abdominal assessment is unrelated to Sjogren's and RA.

B is incorrect because dry nose and mouth are common with Sjogren's syndrome and can lead to a stuffy nose, which can make breathing difficult and uncomfortable. Saline nasal spray can help keep the nasal passages moist and facilitate easier breathing.

C is incorrect because renal function is unrelated to Sjogren's and RA.

13. The client with rheumatoid arthritis (RA) has been identified by the nurse as having poor body image. Which finding demonstrates that goals for the client problem are progressing towards being met?

A. Attends book club meetings

B. Positive outlook of life

C. Takes medications as prescribed

D. Protects joints by using assistive devices at home

Rationale:

Correct answer: A

Rheumatoid arthritis (RA) is an autoimmune form of arthritis that affects wrists, small joints of the hands, knuckles, and other joints. It is characterized by swelling, pain, and decreased mobility of the joints. Patients with poor body image usually avoid being in public, so attendance at book club meetings would indicate the goal is being met.

B is incorrect because a positive outlook on life is appropriate but does not indicate a goal being met related to poor body image.

C is incorrect because taking medications as prescribed is appropriate but does not indicate a goal being met related to poor body image.

D is incorrect because using assistive devices is appropriate for physical health and safety but is unrelated to body image. Assistive devices may need to be used outside of the home, as well. A patient with poor body image may be at risk for avoiding use of assistive devices in public due to concerns about what others will think of them.

14. What is the most appropriate education the nurse can provide for the patient starting treatment with etanercept?

    A. Subcutaneous injection administration
    B. Annual chest X-ray
    C. Medications taken with food
    D. Applying heat to injection site

Rationale:

Correct answer: A

Etanercept is administered for autoimmune diseases that interferes with tumor necrosis factor (TNF) and is given by subcutaneous injection two times a week. The patient should be taught how to self-administer the medication. Side effects include headache, rhinitis, upper respiratory infection, and injection site reaction. Etanercept can also cause thrombocytopenia and leukopenia.

B is incorrect because an annual chest X-ray is not necessary for etanercept.

C is incorrect because taking etanercept with food is not necessary.

D is incorrect because applying heat to the injection site is not necessary for etanercept.

15. What non-pharmacologic comfort measure does the nurse recommend for the patient with rheumatoid arthritis (RA) who has an acutely inflamed and painful joint?

    A. Consume more dairy products
    B. Apply ice packs to the affected joint

C. Apply a splint to the affected joint

D. Use a paraffin wax dip on the affected joint

Rationale:

Correct answer: B

Rheumatoid arthritis (RA) is an autoimmune form of arthritis that affects wrists, small joints of the hands, knuckles, and other joints. Acute inflammation is treated best with ice packs.

A is incorrect because rheumatoid arthritis symptoms may flare in response to certain proteins found in milk products.

C is incorrect because splints are used to immobilize injured joints, not for RA inflammation.

D is incorrect because wax dip provides warmth which is for chronic stiffness and pain.

16. A patient with systemic sclerosis has taut skin, affecting how the patient opens their mouth. The nurse has consulted with the registered dietitian, but what other consultation should be facilitated by the nurse?

   A. Dentist
   B. Massage therapist
   C. Occupational therapy
   D. Physical therapy

Rationale:

Correct answer: A

Systemic sclerosis or scleroderma is a disease of the connective tissues that leads to fibrosis, vasomotor disturbance, skin atrophy, and atrophy of tissues, muscles, and organs including the lungs, kidney, and heart. Due to taut skin around the mouth, the patient may not be able to perform effective dental hygiene, so the nurse should facilitate consultation with a dentist.

B is incorrect because a massage therapist may facilitate facial motor movement but is not as important as oral hygiene.

C is incorrect because occupational therapy is aimed at helping patients regain function for performing household activities.

D is incorrect because physical therapy will not help the mouth as specifically as a dentist.

17. A patient with gout is learning dietary strategies from the nurse to prevent exacerbations. Which is the most appropriate statement by the nurse?

   A. "Drink 2 liters of water daily."
   B. "Avoid butter and buttermilk."
   C. "Liver is an excellent source of dietary iron."
   D. "Avoid low-fat yogurt."

Rationale:

Correct answer: A

Gout is due to uric acid metabolized in a defective manner which is deposited in small bones such as in the feet, causing joint pain, swelling, and limitation of movement. Patients with gout commonly develop kidney stones, so increasing water intake can prevent kidney stones from occurring. Patients should avoid foods rich in purines, such as organ meats, fish, alcohol, and sardines. Medications used to treat gout include colchicine with NSAIDs, probenecid, and allopurinol. Obesity, family history, and diuretics can contribute to gout formation.

B is incorrect because butter and buttermilk are not high in purines and do not need to be avoided with gout.

C is incorrect because organ meats should be avoided.

D is incorrect because low-fat yogurt reduces the risk of gout.

18. A client with psoriatic arthritis was just prescribed golimumab. What is the most important information the nurse should teach about taking the medication?

   A. "Avoid crowds and sick people."
   B. "Sit upright for an hour after taking the medication."
   C. "This medication could cause you to lose hair."
   D. "If pain is severe, you can double your dose."

Rationale:

Correct answer: A

Psoriatic arthritis is a type of arthritis commonly seen in patients diagnosed with psoriasis. Golimumab is a disease-modifying antirheumatic drug (DMARD) immunosuppressant administered for autoimmune types of arthritis. Due to the immunosuppressant action, the patient should be taught to avoid crowds and sick people to prevent serious and opportunistic infection.

B is incorrect because sitting upright is unrelated to golimumab. Patients taking bisphosphonates must remain upright after taking their medication.

C is incorrect because hair loss is unrelated to golimumab. Hair loss is a side effect of some antineoplastic and chemotherapy medications.

D is incorrect because golimumab dosing should not be doubled.

19. A patient with fibromyalgia who has just been prescribed duloxetine hydrochloride is calling the nurse at the clinic to ask why they need to take an antidepressant. What is the best response by the nurse?

   A. "The sedation will help you sleep."
   B. "Depression often occurs with fibromyalgia."
   C. "The medication works in the brain for decreasing pain."
   D. "I'll contact the ordering healthcare provider and ask for your call to be returned."

Rationale:

Correct answer: C

Fibromyalgia is a syndrome that affects soft tissue and muscles and contributes to muscle pain, sleep disturbance, fatigue, and generalized pain. Duloxetine hydrochloride increases neurotransmitter serotonin as well as norepinephrine release, which can reduce pain due to fibromyalgia. The recommended dosage for fibromyalgia is 60 mg taken PO, once daily.

A is incorrect because duloxetine does not cause sedation. It should be taken in the morning because it can cause insomnia.

B is incorrect because depression does not often occur with fibromyalgia.

D is incorrect because duloxetine is useful in decreasing pain associated with fibromyalgia with or without comorbid depression. The healthcare provider does not need to be called. The nurse should provide information to the patient and not delay communication.

20. The nurse in the clinic is assessing clients with osteoporosis. Which client would not be advised to take bisphosphonates?

    A. 55-year-old female patient with diabetes and serum creatinine 0.9 mg/dL
    B. 63-year-old female patient with recent fall and compression fractures of vertebrae
    C. 68-year-old male with history of hypertension taking verapamil daily
    D. 59-year-old female patient who is unable to sit up due to spinal cord injury

Rationale:

Correct answer: D

Osteoporosis causes bones to become brittle and porous due to loss of bone tissue, usually due to hormonal changes or deficiencies in vitamin D or calcium. Both men and women can develop osteoporosis, and women are more likely to. Bisphosphonates, when administered, require the patient sit up for a period of 30 minutes to an hour afterward, so the patient who is unable to sit up is not the best candidate for the medication. If chest discomfort is experienced within 30 minutes, the medication should be discontinued and the healthcare provider should be notified as this can be a sign of esophageal erosion, a serious side effect of bisphosphonates. The ages of these patients are insignificant for bisphosphonate use.

A is incorrect because diabetes is unrelated to bisphosphonates. Creatinine tests renal function, and the normal level is 0.7-1.4 mg/dL. A diabetic patient with normal renal function is a candidate for bisphosphonate therapy.

B is incorrect because a recent fall and fracture are not contraindications for bisphosphonate use.

C is incorrect because hypertension is unrelated and calcium channel blockers do not interact with bisphosphonates.

21. A patient with a lower extremity fracture is treated with balanced skeletal traction. Which assessment finding would warrant the nurse urgently notifying the healthcare provider?

A. Blood pressure increase to 132/88 mmHg

B. Traction weights resting on floor

C. Pin sites oozing clear fluid

D. Capillary refill less than three seconds

Rationale:

Correct answer: B

Skeletal traction is applied to realign fractured bones and prevent further injury prior to surgery. Weights are attached to pins inserted into the patient's bones. The weights must remain suspended in order to properly apply traction to the bones. Weights resting on the floor should not be manipulated by the nurse. The weights must be reapplied by the healthcare provider.

A is incorrect because blood pressure is only slightly elevated and could be due to pain. This BP should be compared to earlier measurements and should be monitored for further increase. The nurse should expect to treat pain and muscle spasms in the patient in traction.

C is incorrect because clear fluid oozing from pin sites is normal. Pin sites should be assessed and cleaned with half-strength hydrogen peroxide every eight hours. Pus-colored or foul-smelling drainage is a sign of infection at the pin sites.

D is incorrect because the capillary refill is normal. This needs to be assessed frequently on the affected leg, and delayed refill time can be a sign of circulatory compromise.

22. A patient is admitted to the emergency department with a crush injury to the right lower extremity. When the patient reports numbness and tingling of the injured leg, what is the first action the nurse should take?

    A. Assess pedal pulses

    B. Apply oxygen with nasal cannula

    C. Increase IV fluid rate

    D. Apply traction

Rationale:

Correct answer: A

A crush injury is caused by an object that compresses a portion of the body and causes trauma. This can lead to compartment syndrome, which is characterized by numbness and tingling, which often leads to irreversible motor or vascular damage without intervention. The nurse needs to assess for equal pedal pulses, and if decreased on the injured side, the healthcare provider must be notified.

B is incorrect because oxygen is indicated for signs of hypoxia; this patent is exhibiting signs of neurovascular compromise, which will not be corrected with oxygen.

C is incorrect because IV fluids will help treat low blood circulation, but pulses must be assessed first.

D is incorrect because it is not within the nurse's scope of practice to apply traction.

23. A patient who had a cast applied to the wrist several days ago tells the nurse the cast has become loose and unsupportive. What is the best response by the nurse?

    A. "Keep the arm above your heart."
    B. "The cast will loosen as muscles atrophy."
    C. "A bandage can be wrapped around the cast to prevent slipping."
    D. "Since the swelling has decreased, you will need a new cast."

Rationale:

Correct answer: D.

A cast is applied to a fracture in order to ensure fractured bones stay in alignment and aid in proper healing. Swelling can be present in soft tissues when a cast is applied initially, so once swelling decreases and two or more fingers can be placed between the skin and the cast, the cast will need to be replaced.

A is incorrect because the purpose of elevating the arm is to reduce swelling. This patient's arm swelling has already decreased, so elevation is not necessary and will not help the cast to fit better.

B is incorrect because muscle atrophy does not occur in several days. Muscle atrophy under a cast occurs after several weeks.

C is incorrect because a bandage will not help. If the cast is too loose, the only correction is application of a new cast.

24. A patient recovering after above the knee amputation reports pain in the foot of the surgical side. After reviewing the medications ordered for the patient, which medication should the nurse give first?

    A. IV morphine
    B. Oral acetaminophen
    C. IV calcitonin
    D. Oral ibuprofen

Rationale:

Correct answer: C

Amputations are performed to remove an extremity due to infection, crush injury, non-healing wounds, and poor circulation, among several other indications. The patient who has an extremity amputated may report burning, cramping, or crushing pain, which are manifestations of phantom limb pain. Intravenous calcitonin can reduce the symptoms of phantom limb pain, which may occur immediately post-op up to three months following amputation. Non-pharmacologic treatments to relieve phantom limb pain include use of a mirror box, acupuncture, and nerve stimulation.

A is incorrect because IV morphine will not be as effective as calcitonin. Morphine is a narcotic that can also cause other adverse reactions, so it should only be used if the calcitonin is ineffective for treating the phantom limb pain.

B is incorrect because acetaminophen is not used for phantom limb pain.

D is incorrect because ibuprofen is not used for phantom limb pain.

25. A patient recovering after below the knee amputation has their care planned by the nurse. Which intervention should be included in the plan of care?

    A. Placing pillows between the knees
    B. Range of motion exercise
    C. Prophylactic antibiotics
    D. Strict bedrest

Rationale:

Correct answer: B

Amputations are performed to remove an extremity due to infection, crush injury, non-healing wounds, and poor circulation, among several other indications. Range of motion exercises should be performed for prevention of contractions of the extremity and in preparation for prosthesis.

A is incorrect because pillows are placed *under* the affected limb for support. Pillows are placed *between* the knees for hip replacement post-operative patients.

C is incorrect because antibiotics are not indicated unless signs of infection are present, such as pus or foul-odor drainage oozing from the dressing, elevated temperature, chills, or elevated white blood cells.

D is incorrect because the patient should not be on strict bedrest. The patient is at risk for blood clots, depression, atelectasis, and contracture, so the patient should be up out of the bed and moving as soon as possible.

26. A patient with rotator cuff injury is being assessed by the inpatient nurse. Which finding should the nurse expect?

    A. Unable to maintain adduction longer than 30 seconds on the affected side
    B. Shoulder pain relieved by overhead stretching and at night
    C. Unable to abduct affected arm at shoulder
    D. Referred pain to affected shoulder and opposite arm

Rationale:

Correct answer: C

Rotator cuff injury affects muscles and tendons supporting the shoulder joint and keeping the humeral head in the socket, causing aching shoulder pain which is worse when pressure is applied. A patient who has a rotator cuff injury cannot abduct the arm at the shoulder, which is determined by a drop arm test.

A is incorrect because *adduction* is not affected. Adduction is the normal position of the shoulder joint. If *abduction* cannot be held for 30 seconds, this can be a sign of rotator cuff injury.

B is incorrect because the pain associated with rotator cuff injury is often worse at night, causing sleep disturbances. Overhead stretching is often very painful to the lateral portion of the shoulder and the upper arm.

D is incorrect because pain is not referred to the opposite shoulder with rotator cuff injury.

27. A client with cast to the left arm calls the phone triage nurse about swelling and a tight feeling to the cast. What is the best response by the nurse?

    A. "Elevate the arm on pillows and apply ice to the cast."
    B. "Take ibuprofen until swelling subsides."
    C. "Swelling and a tight feeling are normal. Call back if improvement is not noted by tomorrow."
    D. "Come in to the clinic and the healthcare provider will check it."

Rationale:

Correct answer: D

A cast is applied to a fracture in order to ensure fractured bones stay in alignment and aid in proper healing. Swelling can be present in soft tissues when a cast is applied initially; however, compartment syndrome can develop. The nurse should tell the patient to come into the clinic to have it checked immediately to prevent permanent damage. Signs of compartment syndrome include decreased pulse, pallor, tingling, inability to move distal to the cast, and pain.

A is incorrect because elevation of the arm may help by decreasing blood flow to the arm, but this is only a temporary measure. The safest action is to have the patient come in to be seen immediately. If circulation is compromised, the cast will need to be removed, and any delay could cause loss of limb. Ice will not help when a cast is applied because the cold will not reach the limb through the cast.

B is incorrect because although it *is* within the nurse's scope of practice to instruct the patient to take over-the-counter medications, and ibuprofen *may* reduce swelling, this is not the safest action.

C is incorrect because swelling and tightness are *not* normal. The cast needs to be checked and circulation needs to be assessed to determine if removal of the cast is indicated. Upon arrival at the healthcare facility, the patient must be assessed for ability to move fingers, capillary refill, pulses, sensation, and skin color to determine circulation. If cast removal is delayed, the patient may lose the arm.

28. A patient had a long-leg cast placed for fractures last week. They tell the nurse it is difficult to breathe, and they feel lightheaded. Which is the next action the nurse should take?

    A. Auscultate anterior and posterior lung fields

    B. Administer oxygen to maintain higher than 92%

    C. Check blood glucose level

    D. Have the patient take deep breaths

Rationale:

Correct answer: B

Fractures of bones can lead to bone fragments and dispersion of bone contents including blood clots and fat cells. The patient has symptoms that are consistent with pulmonary embolism, which could be due to the fracture or the immobility due to the long cast. Oxygen must be administered, and pulse oximetry should be monitored. Once oxygen is applied, the nurse should then auscultate lung fields.

A is incorrect because when signs of hypoxia are present (difficult breathing and lightheadedness), oxygen delivery should not be delayed. Auscultation of lung fields should be performed after oxygen therapy is initiated.

C is incorrect because checking blood glucose will not help. Hypoglycemia is not likely with long bone fracture or cast application, and there is no indication that this patient is diabetic or on insulin.

D is incorrect because taking deep breaths will help *after* oxygen has been applied.

29. A patient recovering from vertebroplasty is educated by the nurse. Which patient statement demonstrates a need for further education?

    A. "I can drive myself home."

    B. "I will monitor the puncture site for infection."

    C. "I will begin walking tomorrow and slowly increase activity."

    D. "The dressing can be removed the day following discharge."

Rationale:

Correct answer: A

Vertebroplasty is performed to stabilize a compression fracture of the spine with bone cement injected into the vertebrae. The fractures are usually due to osteoporosis. Expected outcomes of vertebroplasty include decreased pain and increased spinal strength with better ability to perform ADLS. For the first 24 hours following vertebroplasty, the patient should not drive or operate machinery.

B is incorrect because monitoring for infection is appropriate. Redness, swelling, or warmth at the injection site should be reported to the healthcare provider.

C is incorrect because walking and activity are appropriate. Decreased ability to move the arms or legs is a sign of nerve damage, a rare complication of vertebropplasty, and should be reported immediately.

D is incorrect because removing the dressing the day after discharge is appropriate.

30. A patient has been prescribed skeletal traction with external fixation, and the nurse is planning their care. Which intervention should be included in the care plan to decrease risk of infection?

   A. Wash traction ropes and sockets daily
   B. Release traction twice a day for 30 minutes
   C. Gently rest traction weights on the floor during position changes to minimize pain
   D. Perform pin care every eight hours

Rationale:

Correct answer: D

Skeletal traction is applied to realign fractured bones and prevent further injury prior to surgery. Weights are attached to pin sites inserted into the patient's bones. The weights must remain suspended, and the nurse should take caution not to bump or manipulate the weights, as this can cause increased pain or disrupt the pull of the traction. Pin sites of the external fixator should be cared for with half-strength hydrogen peroxide every eight hours in order to prevent infection.

A is incorrect because traction ropes should not be removed without the healthcare provider's order and cleaning the ropes will not prevent infection. The ropes are attached to pins, which come into direct contact with the patient, so the *pins* are the concern for proper cleaning.

B is incorrect because traction should not be released by the nurse, and this would not prevent infection.

C is incorrect because traction weights should not be placed on the floor. Any patient equipment that comes into contact with the floor increases the risk for infection.

31. A nursing student is caring for a patient with rheumatoid arthritis (RA). Which of the following are facts about RA? (Select all that apply.)

    A. Only single joints are affected

    B. Inflammation is caused by antibodies

    C. It is an autoimmune process

    D. Morning stiffness is rare

    E. Permanent damage is inevitable

Rationale:

Correct answer: B, C

Rheumatoid arthritis (RA) is an autoimmune form of arthritis that affects wrists, small joints of the hands, knuckles, and other joints. It is characterized by swelling, pain, and decreased mobility of the joints. This chronic autoimmune disorder occurs when the body fails to recognize its own cells. Normal antibodies attack healthy cells and tissues in autoimmune disorders.

A is incorrect because RA can affect many joints. Other body systems may be affected too, such as the skin, eyes, the heart, lungs, and blood vessels.

D is incorrect because morning stiffness with RA is common.

E is incorrect because early, aggressive treatment can prevent permanent damage.

32. The nurse caring for a 44-year-old female patient with rheumatoid arthritis (RA) is teaching her about methotrexate (MTX). What information should be included by the nurse? (Select all that apply.)

    A. "Avoid over-the-counter medications with ibuprofen."

    B. "Pain relief effects may take several weeks."

    C. "MTX is safe to take while pregnant or breastfeeding."

D. "Avoid large crowds and sick people."

E. "Folic acid may reduce side effects."

Rationale:

Correct answer: B, D, E

Rheumatoid arthritis (RA) is an autoimmune form of arthritis that affects wrists, small joints of the hands, knuckles, and other joints. It is characterized by swelling, pain, and decreased mobility of the joints. MTX is an anti-rheumatic drug and first line treatment for RA. It can take up to six weeks for the medication to effectively relieve pain. Large crowds and sick people should be avoided due to immunosuppression from MTX. Side effects include nausea, vomiting, diarrhea, stomatitis, hepatic, and renal dysfunction. Folic acid can reduce side effects for some patients. MTX is also used to treat acute lymphocytic leukemia, psoriasis, and sickle cell anemia.

A is incorrect because ibuprofen is safe to take with MTX. Liver toxicity is a risk, so acetaminophen-containing medications should be avoided.

C is incorrect because MTX is contraindicated in pregnancy and breastfeeding.

33. A patient recently diagnosed with fibromyalgia refuses to take her medications. Which non-pharmacologic measures should the nurse suggest in order to manage the patient's condition? (Select all that apply.)

    A. Acupuncture treatments
    B. Daily stretching
    C. Nutritional supplement beverages
    D. Tai chi exercises
    E. Aerobics

Rationale:

Correct answer: A, B, D

Fibromyalgia is a syndrome that affects soft tissue and muscles and contributes to muscle pain, sleep disturbance, fatigue, and pain. Non-pharmacologic measures that can help control fibromyalgia symptoms include acupuncture, stretching, swimming, biking, massage, and hypnosis. Yoga and Tai chi are beneficial low-impact stretching activities that can also be beneficial in increasing movement and decreasing pain.

C is incorrect because nutritional supplement beverages can have interactions with many medications and are not recommended for fibromyalgia.

E is incorrect because aerobics are high impact and are not recommended for fibromyalgia.

34. The nurse in the rheumatology clinic is assessing clients for late manifestations of rheumatoid arthritis (RA). Which of the following does the nurse look for? (Select all that apply.)

   A. Anorexia
   B. Felty's syndrome
   C. Joint deformity
   D. Low grade fever
   E. Weight loss

Rationale:

Correct answer: B, C, E

Rheumatoid arthritis (RA) is an autoimmune form of arthritis that affects wrists, small joints of the hands, knuckles, and other joints. It is characterized by swelling, pain, and decreased mobility of the joints. Felty's syndrome is a complication of long-term RA and includes enlarged spleen and abnormally low WBC count. Joint deformity, organ involvement, anemia, osteoporosis, weight loss, and extreme fatigue are all late manifestations of RA.

A is incorrect because anorexia is an early manifestation of RA.

D is incorrect because low-grade fever is an early manifestation of RA.

35. A 73-year-old patient is returned to the nursing unit after hip replacement surgery. The patient is disoriented and restless. Which actions can be delegated to the unlicensed assistive personnel (UAP) by the nurse? (Select all that apply.)

   A. Apply an abduction pillow to patient's legs
   B. Assess skin under the abduction pillow straps

251

C. Elevate heels off the bed with pillows

D. Determine ability of the patient to get up by monitoring cognition

E. Take and document vital signs

Rationale:

Correct answer: A, C, E

Total hip replacement is a surgical procedure performed to replace a joint damaged by osteoarthritis, or fracture, along with several other causes. It is within the scope of practice of the UAP to apply the abduction pillow, elevate the heels, and take and document vital signs. Routine tasks that routinely occur in the care of patients and are performed according to an established set of steps can be delegated to the UAP.

B is incorrect because assessment of skin is the responsibility of the nurse. Any task that requires assessment should not be delegated.

D is incorrect because determining the patient's ability to get out of bed requires nursing judgment and is the responsibility of the nurse.

36. Clients with connective tissue diseases are being assessed by the clinic nurse. Which diseases are correctly paired with their clinical findings? (Select all that apply.)

   A. Dry, scaly skin rash - Systemic lupus erythematosus (SLE)
   B. Esophageal dysmotility - Systemic sclerosis
   C. Excess hydrochloric acid - Gout
   D. Foot drop, paresthesia - Osteoarthritis
   E. Organ damage caused by vasculitis - Rheumatoid arthritis

Rationale:

Correct answer: A, B, E

SLE is most often manifested by dry, scaly skin rash. Systemic sclerosis leads to motility problems of the esophagus. Rheumatoid arthritis causes vasculitis and organ damage.

C is incorrect because hyperuricemia leads to gout. Excess hydrochloric acid in gastric secretions can lead to stomach and intestinal ulcers.

D is incorrect because RA leads to foot drop and paresthesia.

37. The clinic nurse is reviewing medication records for patients with gout. Which gout classifications and their corresponding drug treatments are correctly matched? (Select all that apply.)

    A. Allopurinol - Acute gout

    B. Colchicine - Acute gout

    C. Febuxostat - Chronic gout

    D. Indomethacin - Acute gout

    E. Probenecid - Chronic gout

Rationale:

Correct answer: B, C, D, E

Gout is due to uric acid metabolized in a defective manner which is deposited in small bones such as in the feet, causing arthritis and pain. Colchicine and indomethacin are for use in acute gout. Febuxostat blocks xanthine oxidase (which lowers uric acid levels in blood), and probenecid helps urine excretion of uric acid and is for use in chronic gout.

A is incorrect because allopurinol is for use in chronic gout as it blocks the formation of uric acid. Aspirin should be avoided when taking allopurinol because it decreases the effectiveness of this drug.

38. A patient with a history of systemic sclerosis (SSc) is admitted to the medical unit. Which comfort measures for this patient can be delegated to the unlicensed assistive personnel (UAP) by the nurse? (Select all that apply.)

    A. Collaborate with the registered dietician for meals

    B. Inspect skin and note ulcerated areas

    C. Keep the room at comfortable temperature

    D. Place a foot cradle on the bed to lift sheets

    E. Remind patient to keep the head of the bed elevated after meals

Rationale:

Correct answer: C, D, E

Systemic sclerosis, or scleroderma, is a disease of the connective tissues that leads to fibrosis, vasomotor disturbance, skin atrophy, and atrophy of tissues, muscles, and organs including the lungs, kidneys, and heart. It is within the scope of practice for the UAP to maintain a warm, comfortable temperature in the room, place the foot cradle on the bed, and remind the patient to elevate the head of the bed after meals.

A is incorrect because collaboration with the registered dietician is the responsibility of the nurse.

B is incorrect because any form of assessment, such as inspecting skin, is the responsibility of the nurse.

39. The home health nurse is performing a home assessment for a client with rheumatoid arthritis (RA). Which of the following can the nurse suggest to assist the patient in maintaining independence? (Select all that apply.)

    A. Grab bars for high items
    B. Long-handled bath brush
    C. Soft rocker chair
    D. Toothbrush with a large handle
    E. Wheelchair cushion

Rationale:

Correct answer: A, B, D

Rheumatoid arthritis (RA) is an autoimmune form of arthritis that affects wrists, small joints of the hands, knuckles, and other joints. It is characterized by swelling, pain, and decreased mobility of the joints. Grab bars for high items, long-handled bath brushes, and large-handled toothbrushes are all appropriate modifications for the patient with RA to use for ADLs.

C is incorrect because the soft rocker chair is a comfort measure and does not increase independence.

E is incorrect because the wheelchair cushion is a comfort measure and does not increase independence.

40. The home health nurse is visiting a client who had a hip replacement last week. The client is still using a walker and using partial weight bearing. What safety precautions should the nurse recommend? (Select all that apply.)

A. Elevated toilet seat

B. Grab bars by the toilet and in the shower

C. Use affected leg to step into vehicle first

D. Remove throw rugs from the home

E. Use of a shower chair

Rationale:

Correct answer: A, B, D, E

Total hip replacement is a surgical procedure performed to replace a joint damaged by osteoarthritis or fracture, along with several other causes. An elevated toilet seat, grab bars, removal of throw rugs, and a shower chair are all appropriate safety precautions for the patient who has had a hip replacement. The patient may also need assistive devices to help with putting on socks and shoes. The patient should be taught about appropriate leg positioning for the first 12 weeks after surgery: flexion no more than 90 degrees and avoid internal rotation of the affected leg.

C is incorrect because the patient is partial weight bearing and cannot step in to the vehicle with the affected leg first. A stool should be used near the vehicle and the patient should step in with the unaffected leg.

NCLEX-RN - MED-SURG: ONCOLOGY - 40 QUESTIONS

1. The nurse is evaluating an oncology patient's chart. They note that the patient is suffering from lung cancer and has a tumor about 4cm in size and associated pneumonitis. The tumor does not invade the entire lung and does not have lymph node involvement or distant metastasis. Using the TNM staging system, how would the nurse characterize this cancer patient's tumor?

    A. T3 N3 M1
    B. T2 N0 M0
    C. T1 N1 M0
    D. T2 N1 M0

Rationale:

Correct answer: B

The TNM tumor staging method involves tumor size (T), node involvement (N), and distant metastasis (M). This patient has a tumor 4cm in size but locally contained in one section of the lung, giving it a rating of T2. Since there is no nodal involvement or metastasis, both N and M are 0.

A is incorrect. T3 N3 M1 describes a tumor great than 7cm, metastasis in all contralateral lymph nodes, and distant metastasis.

C is incorrect. T1 N1 M1 describes a tumor that is self-contained and less than 3cm in size, some lymph node involvement, and no metastasis.

D is incorrect. T2 N1 M0 indicates a tumor which is between 3 and 7cm in size, has some lymph node involvement, but no distant metastasis.

2. The incoming nurse is told in a report that their patient has been struggling with asymptomatic chemotherapy-induced anemia. The nurse understands that the patient will likely need a blood transfusion if:

   A. Hemoglobin drops below 8.0 g/dL
   B. Leukocytes drop below 4,000/mm³
   C. Hemoglobin drops below 10 g/dL
   D. Absolute neutrophil count is 1000/mm³

Rationale:

Correct answer: A

Hemoglobin levels are considered concerning and may require blood transfusions when below 8g/dL. Normal hemoglobin levels are 13.5 to 17.5 g/dL for men and 12 to 15.5 for women.

B is incorrect. While 4000/mm³ is on the low end of appropriate leukocyte levels, and this may be an effect of chemotherapy, this is not directly related to anemia, nor is it an indication for a blood transfusion.

C is incorrect. 10 g/dL is considered a low hemoglobin for both men and women, but since this patient is asymptomatic, they will not likely need a blood transfusion at this juncture.

D is incorrect. When ANC drops below 1000/mm³, this is called neutropenia. This is a side effect of chemotherapy and it increases the patient's risk for infection, but this does not necessitate a blood transfusion.

3. The nurse is caring for a cancer patient who is undergoing chemotherapy. The patient is losing weight as a result of intermittent nausea and vomiting. The nurse encourages which of the following interventions to reduce nausea? (Select all that apply.)

   A. Encourage using hot sauce and flavorful herbs for unappetizing foods
   B. Consume small, frequent meals
   C. Provide meals that are served at room temperature
   D. Brush teeth midday rather than upon awakening in the morning
   E. Consume high-fat and high-protein foods

Rationale:

Correct answer: B, C, D

Serving small frequent meals served at room temperature and delaying teeth brushing till the midday may reduce nausea.

A is incorrect. Spicy foods and strong herbs may aggravate nausea in the patient receiving chemotherapy.

E is incorrect. High-fat foods are especially nauseating for those prone to upset stomach.

4. The nurse is discussing immunity with a student nurse. Which of the following statements by the student demonstrates an understanding about immunity?

    A. "The cell-mediated immune response is an example of adaptive immunity."
    B. "An example of artificially acquired active immunity is when a mother passes antibodies through the placenta to the fetus."
    C. Naturally acquired active immunity occurs after two or more exposures to a disease or foreign antigen.
    D. "The flu vaccine is naturally acquired active immunity."

Rationale:

Correct answer: A

Cell-mediated immunity is a good example of adaptive immunity. This type of immunity is spurred by cytokines and T-lymphocytes and doesn't involve antibodies.

B is incorrect. Antibodies passed from mother to baby via the placenta or breastmilk is naturally acquired passive immunity.

C is incorrect. In naturally acquired active immunity, the body produces specific antibodies during infection by a virus or bacterium, and memory cells remain in the bloodstream after recovery to give a faster secondary response if the same antigen is encountered again, making the individual immune to that pathogen.

D is incorrect. Vaccines are artificially acquired adaptive immunity. (An individual is given an injection of a small dose of weakened pathogen to stimulate the immune system to produce specific antibodies against that infection.)

5. While the nurse is caring for their patient with a large breast tumor, the patient reports some difficulty breathing. Upon examination, the nurse notes that the patient has a swollen face and neck, nasal congestion, and a hoarse voice. The nurse would most likely believe which of the following conditions is occurring in their patient?

   A. Spinal cord compression
   B. Hodgkin's lymphoma
   C. Superior vena cava syndrome
   D. Septic shock

Rationale:

Correct answer: C

Since this patient's cancerous tumor is located in the chest region, pressure from the tumor may result in the obstruction of flow to and/or from the superior vena cava. Common clinical presentations of Superior vena cava syndrome include blurred vision, hoarse voice, stridor, dyspnea, and nasal congestion. Patients may also experience a pleural effusion or light-headedness.

A is incorrect because spinal cord compression develops when the spinal cord is compressed by bone fragments from a vertebral fracture, a tumor, abscess, ruptured intervertebral disc or another lesion. Symptoms include back pain, paralysis, areas of increased or decreased sensation, and urinary or fecal incontinence.

B is incorrect because the symptoms of Hodgkin's lymphoma include fever, night sweats, and weight loss. The patient may also have painless, enlarged lymph nodes near the next, axillae, or inguinal area.

D is incorrect because the symptoms of septic shock include organ injury related to infection along with low blood pressure, tachypnea, altered WBC (abnormally low or high), and tachycardia.

6. The nurse is caring for a patient with an epidural tumor. The patient reports new onset of inability to feel the lower extremities along with severe back pain. What is the priority action by the nurse?

   A. Evaluate and manage the patient's pain

B. Observe for signs of urinary retention

C. Aid the patient in performing personal hygiene care

D. Maintain strict bed rest

Rationale:

Correct answer: D

The patient is showing signs of spinal cord compression. Strict bed rest should be maintained while spinal stability is evaluated. Allowing the patient to ambulate or get out of bed increases the risk for paralysis or other permanent neurological damage.

A is incorrect because preventing paralysis by maintaining bed rest is a greater priority than pain control.

B is incorrect because although spinal cord compression can cause urinary retention, this is a non-life-threatening symptom which is not as important as maintaining bed rest.

C is incorrect because assistance with hygiene is not a priority when spinal cord compression is suspected.

7. When caring for a patient diagnosed with lung cancer, the nurse notes the patient will be receiving a wedge resection tomorrow. The nurse is aware that what part of the lung will be removed?

   A. A lung lobe

   B. A whole lung

   C. A small, localized segment near the superficial surface of the lung

   D. A segment of the lung containing bronchioles and alveoli

Rationale:

Correct answer: C

During a wedge resection, a small, localized portion of the lung will be removed. This section will be close to the surface of the lung. A margin of healthy tissue around the sample will be removed as well. This is often done when removal of an entire lung lobe would impact respirations too much. A wedge resection is the smallest amount of lung tissue that can be removed in the treatment of lung cancer.

A is incorrect because this describes a lobectomy. Humans generally have five lung lobes: three on the right and two on the left. If a wedge resection or segmentectomy is not sufficient to remove the cancer or diseased portion of lung, a lobectomy will be performed.

B is incorrect because removal of an entire lung, a pneumonectomy, is a much larger procedure with greater risks than a wedge resection.

D is incorrect because it describes a segmentectomy.

8. The nurse is caring for a chemotherapy patient with an absolute neutrophil count (ANC) of 900. The patient has had poor nutritional intake over the past five days. The patient states, "All I want to eat is cheese, crackers, grapes, and pickles." How should the nurse reply?

   A. "The goal is to increase your calorie intake, so I will order those foods for you."
   B. "I can get you some crackers, but the other foods you requested are not safe because of your neutropenia."
   C. "I can order you some crackers, but I suggest you also try the plain mashed potatoes and boiled, lightly-seasoned chicken."
   D. "If we don't boost your calorie intake you may need to start tube feeding."

Rationale:

Correct answer: C

Neutrophils make up the majority of circulating white blood cells and serve as the primary defense against infections by destroying bacteria and viruses in the blood. A normal absolute neutrophil count (ANC) is 1500-8000 cells/microliter. This patient has moderate neutropenia (ANC 1000-1500) and is at moderate risk for infection. Plain mashed potatoes and boiled, light-seasoned chicken are the best meal option for this neutropenic patient. Potatoes are easy to eat for patients with oral discomfort. Lightly seasoned, boiled chicken is fully cooked and poses no risk to the patient. Offering to order crackers, as well, is therapeutic because it acknowledges the patient's wishes.

A is incorrect because some cheeses are unsafe to serve to the neutropenic patient as they may increase risk for infection. Fresh fruit, such as grapes, may contain bacteria, and should also be avoided on a neutropenic diet. Pickled foods can be irritating to the mouth, especially for chemotherapy patients who often experience stomatitis and sores in the mouth.

B is incorrect because (although it is a true statement) crackers alone will not meet the patient's dietary needs.

D is incorrect because although it may be a true statement, the nurse should communicate therapeutically by acknowledging the patient's wishes and making alternative, healthy suggestions.

9. A patient with an absolute neutrophil count of 750 is being transported from the hospital room for a procedure in a different hospital department. The patient has been complaining of chills and has had difficulty ambulating due to muscle weakness from chemotherapy. The nurse should ensure the patient uses which item at all times during transport?

   A. A gait belt to prevent falls
   B. Warmed blankets to maintain body heat
   C. Portable EKG monitor
   D. A face mask

Rationale:

Correct answer: D

Neutropenic patients are at an increased risk of acquiring an infection. Extra steps, such as wearing a face mask, should be taken to prevent inhalation of airborne infectious agents, especially when being transported through the hospital, where chance for exposure is increased.

A is incorrect. When being transported from the unit to another area of the hospital, the patent should be transported in a wheelchair or on a stretcher, so a gait belt is unnecessary.

B is incorrect. Warm blankets provide comfort and do indeed help maintain patient heat. However, warmth is not as much of a priority as reducing risk for infection.

C is incorrect because continuous EKG monitoring is not required for a chemotherapy patient with neutropenia.

10. When preparing to discuss treatment options with a patient diagnosed with leukemia, which of the following will the nurse not anticipate to be included by the health care provider?

    A. Irradiated red blood cell transfusion

    B. Chemotherapy

    C. Hematopoietic stem cell transplantation

    D. Radioisotope therapy

Rationale:

Correct answer: A

Leukemia is a neoplastic disease that affects blood-forming tissues of the bone marrow, spleen, and lymph nodes. Leukemia is characterized by destruction of at least one type of white blood cell and its precursors. The transfusion of irradiated red blood cells may be used to restore the RBC count in patients with compromised immune systems, but it is not used to treat leukemia.

B is incorrect because chemotherapy is commonly used to treat leukemia.

C is incorrect because hematopoietic stem cell transplantation can be used in addition to either chemotherapy or radiation for the treatment of leukemia.

D is incorrect because radioisotopes can be infused into the bloodstream to affect target tissues that are affected by leukemia.

11. The nurse is providing education to parents of a child receiving chemotherapy. Which of the following statements is appropriate for the nurse to include?

    A. "If your child develops a fever overnight, monitor it closely and bring your child to the clinic first thing in the morning."

    B. "Be sure your child receives the MMR vaccine on schedule to prevent serious infection with the measles."

    C. "Be sure to inspect your child's feet daily to observe for cuts or infections."

    D. "Regularly wash soft toys and security blankets in the washing machine."

Rationale:

Correct answer: D

Children receiving chemotherapy are at increased risk for infection, so parents should be taught about regularly washing items that the child uses frequently. The nurse should also teach the parents about keeping their child away from other children who are sick, avoiding playing with items other children have played with, and disinfecting other toys and surfaces frequently.

A is incorrect because a fever may be the only sign of infection in a child receiving chemotherapy. A fever should be treated as a medical emergency and the parents should be taught to call the healthcare provider on-call or bring the child to the ED immediately.

B is incorrect because a child receiving chemotherapy is immunocompromised and should not receive any live vaccines, such as the MMR vaccine.

C is incorrect because children receiving chemotherapy are not at increased risk specifically related to infections of the feet.

12. The nurse caring for a patient with myelosuppression anticipates performing all of the following nursing actions, except for:

    A. Monitor the patient for fever
    B. Observe for signs of neurological changes
    C. Initiate neutropenic precautions
    D. Administer antibiotics if prescribed

Rationale:

Correct answer: B

While nurses should monitor all patients for level of consciousness changes, observing a patient with myelosuppression for neurological changes is not a priority action.

A is incorrect because patients with myelosuppression are at an increased risk of developing infections. The temperature should be monitored frequently, and any increase in temperature should be reported to the healthcare provider immediately.

C is incorrect because neutropenic precautions are generally initiated in patients with myelosuppression as a preventative measure against infection.

D is incorrect because antibiotics may be prescribed to patients with myelosuppression to aid their weakened immune systems in fighting off infection.

13. The nurse is assessing a client for Hodgkin's disease. Besides noting Reed-Sternberg cells on the lymph node biopsy specimen, what clinical feature will the nurse expect?

    A. Exophthalmos
    B. Urticaria
    C. Presenting age above 45
    D. Painless, enlarged lymph nodes

Rationale:

Correct answer: D

Hodgkin's disease is a type of lymphoma affecting lymphocyte white blood cells. Reeds-Sternberg cells observed in the biopsied lymph node specimen are a classic sign of Hodgkin's disease and are painless, enlarged lymph nodes and movable nodes in the supraclavicular area. Other symptoms include fever, night sweats, and weight loss.

A is incorrect because exophthalmos is an indication of thyroid dysfunction, not Hodgkin's disease.

B is incorrect because urticaria, or itching skin, is not a cardinal sign of Hodgkin's disease. Urticaria is more often seen in kidney disorders, gout, or allergic reactions.

C is incorrect because Hodgkin's lymphoma usually presents in mid-adolescence rather than in adults over 45 years old.

14. A four-year-old is being seen by the oncologist in the office. When the nurse assesses urinary frequency, an irregular mass along the midline of the abdomen, and pallor, the nurse would be most correct in considering which malignancy as the cause?

    A. Hodgkin's lymphoma
    B. Leukemia
    C. Pancreatic cancer
    D. Neuroblastoma

Rationale:

Correct answer: D

This patient is displaying symptoms of a neuroblastoma. These adrenal gland or peritoneal tumors tend to occur in children under 10 years of age and result in urinary frequency and pallor. Tumors are generally located midline of the abdomen. Treatment depends on whether or not the tumor is localized and may include surgical removal along with chemotherapy. Neuroblastoma is the third most common cancer in children after leukemia and brain cancer.

A is incorrect because the patient is not presenting with symptoms of Hodgkin's lymphoma (fever, night sweats, weight loss, non-painful enlarged lymph nodes in the neck, groin, or axilla).

B is incorrect because signs of leukemia include bleeding, bruising, fatigue, fever, and increased risk for infection.

C is incorrect because characteristics of pancreatic cancer include yellow skin, abdominal or back pain, unexplained weight loss, loss of appetite, dark colored urine, and light-colored stool.

15. The nurse is providing pre-operative care for a patient with a brain tumor. Which assessment should be performed every four hours?

   A. Empty and replace the indwelling urinary catheter
   B. Provide a non-stimulating environment
   C. Assess the patient's neurological status
   D. Provide small, bland meals

Rationale:

Correct answer: C

A brain tumor frequently results in changes in the patient's level of consciousness. These early changes in LOC can be indicators of increasing intracranial pressure, which is a sign of worsening patient condition. The nurse should evaluate the patient's mental status using the Glascow Coma scale every four hours before surgery.

A is incorrect because while some patients with brain tumors may have problems with urination, a catheter is not generally needed preoperatively. If an indwelling urinary catheter is in place, the nurse should measure I and O every eight hours, or more frequently. Each time a urinary catheter is replaced, this increases risk for infection, so these should not be changed every four hours.

B is incorrect because providing a quiet environment is appropriate, but this does not need to be done every four hours and is not more important than assessing neurological status.

D is incorrect because NPO status is necessary pre-op before a brain surgery.

16. The pediatric nurse is providing a teaching session to new nurses on the oncology unit. When discussing an osteosarcoma, which of the following statements by a new RN indicates a need for further education?

    A. "At least the child won't experience any pain at the site of the osteosarcoma until after surgery."
    B. "Many parents attribute their children's pain to growing pains."
    C. "Patients may limp on their affected side."
    D. "Most commonly, the osteosarcoma forms in the patient's femur."

Rationale:

Correct answer: A

The nurse must provide education to the new RN about the pain associated with osteosarcoma. This type of bone cancer often occurs in children and is found in the long bones, most commonly the femur.

B is incorrect because pain at the site of the bone cancer can often be misinterpreted as growing pains, or typical aches and pains of childhood. Often, by the time an osteosarcoma is diagnosed, it has spread to the lungs or secondary bones.

C is incorrect because children with an osteosarcoma in the leg often do limp on the affected side.

D is incorrect because the femur is the most common site of osteosarcoma, indicating understanding.

17. The pediatric oncology client is suspected of having developed a case of "Wilm's tumor." It is a priority for the nurse to ensure that which procedure is not performed on this child?

    A. Monitoring of the pediatric patient's blood pressure with an ankle cuff
    B. Taking rectal temperatures
    C. Palpating the abdomen for a mass
    D. Checking the patient's urine for bacteria

Rationale:

Correct answer: C

A Wilm's tumor is a nephroblastoma (cancer of the kidneys), which occurs in children (500 cases annually in the U.S.) and rarely occurs in adults. The nurse should alert other members of the healthcare staff to avoid abdominal palpation. Palpation of Wilm's tumor may causing "seeding" or the spread of the cancerous cells. Symptoms include a painless abdominal mass, loss of appetite, abdominal pain, fever, nausea, and vomiting. Blood in the urine is seen in some cases, and high blood pressure is also seen on some occasions.

A is incorrect because this patient's vital signs should be evaluated per hospital policy. Blood pressure can be monitored on the arm for a patient with Wilm's tumor. However, assessing BP on the ankle is not contraindicated.

B is incorrect because a patient with suspected Wilm's tumor does not necessitate rectal temperatures, but this action is not specifically contraindicated in relation to the Wilm's tumor.

D is incorrect because if a urinary tract infection is suspected, a lab test on urine should be performed. Assessment of this patient's urine is not contraindicated.

18. The oncology nurse notes that the patient is scheduled to receive syngeneic donor stem cells the following morning. The nurse understands that which of the following is true about these stem cells?

   A. There is no risk of graft-versus-host disease
   B. It is possible that the new cells will be cancerous as well
   C. The stem cells originated in the patient's body
   D. This type of stem cell donation cannot be used to treat testicular cancer

Rationale:

Correct answer: A

Syngeneic stem cells are taken from an identical twin (or triplet) of the patient who is to receive the donation. There is no risk of graft-vs-host disease because the patient's body will recognize the donated cells as if they were the patient's own.

B is incorrect because before donating stem cells, donors undergo rigorous medical testing to ensure than the donated cells are cancer-free.

C is incorrect because stem cells which originate in the patient's own body are autologous. Syngeneic stem cells are donated by an identical twin (or triplet) of the recipient.

D is incorrect because syngeneic stem cells donation can be used to treat the following types of cancers: testicular, Hodgkin's and Non-Hodgkin's lymphoma, multiple myeloma, leukemia, severe aplastic anemia, and myelodysplastic syndrome.

19. Following an engraftment procedure, the patient complains of right upper quadrant abdominal pain. The nurse assesses jaundice and palpates an enlarged liver. The nurse suspects which complication of engraftment procedures?

    A. Veno-occlusive disease of the liver

    B. Liver fibrosis

    C. Graft versus host disease

    D. Expected reactions to the procedure

Rationale:

Correct answer: A

Occasionally, following an engraftment, the patient may experience veno-occlusive disease of the hepatic venules. This is a condition in which some of the small veins in the liver are obstructed. Characteristic findings include weight gain due to fluid retention, increased liver size, tenderness near the liver, and raised levels of bilirubin in the blood. The patient will need aggressive treatment via support fluids and symptomatic treatment.

B is incorrect because liver fibrosis is not a typical reaction from engraftment.

C is incorrect because graft versus host disease may occur after an engraftment procedure but is characterized by liver, skin (rash), and GI system damage.

D is incorrect because jaundice, abdominal pain, and a tender, enlarged liver are not expected finding after an engraftment procedure.

20. A female patient is expressing concern over the possibility of developing breast cancer. While providing breast self-examination instructions, which of the following instructions is appropriate?

    A. Perform the breast self-examination on the first day of her period

B. If she is post-menopausal, breast self-examination can be performed once every two months

C. Facing the mirror, examine breasts first with arms at sides, then with arms above head, and finally with hands on hips

D. Perform the breast self-examination when menstrual bleeding is the heaviest

Rationale:

Correct answer: C

Women should exam their breasts at the same time each month, especially when they are soft. The woman should face a mirror and first examine breasts with both arms at her sides, then with both arms above the head, and lastly with her hands on her hips. Other instructions by the nurse should include use of the finger pads of the three middle fingers to palpate breasts to detect unusual growths while lying down, observation for dimpling or retractions on the skin of the breasts, and examination of nipples for discharge, changes or swelling.

A is incorrect because the best time to check breasts for lumps is one week after menstruation begins.

B is incorrect because even post-menopausal clients should be taught to perform the exam once a month, at the same time of the month.

D is incorrect because performing a breast self-examination during menses may be painful, as breasts are often enlarged and tender to the touch during this period.

21. The nurse is caring for a patient being treated for leukemia. Which of the following lab values causes the nurse to consider the patient may be experiencing tumor lysis syndrome?

    A. Potassium 3.3 mEq/L
    B. Hypophosphatemia
    C. Total serum calcium 8.5 mg/L
    D. BUN 8 mg/dL

Rationale:

Correct answer: C

Tumor lysis syndrome (TLS) is a complication of cancer treatment in which numerous cancer cells are killed at a time and their contents are released into the bloodstream. TLS is characterized by hyperkalemia, hyperphosphatemia, hyperuricemia, and elevated BUN. Because calcium levels decrease when phosphate levels increase, the resultant hyperphosphatemia from TLS results in hypocalcemia. Normal total serum calcium is 8.6 - 10.2 mg/L.

TLS occurs most commonly in the treatment of lymphomas and leukemias.

A is incorrect because TLS will present with elevated potassium. Normal potassium is 3.5-5.0 mEq/L.

B is incorrect because TLS is characterized by hyperphosphatemia (increased blood phosphate levels).

D is incorrect because BUN is elevated in TLS. Normal BUN is 10-20 mg/dL.

22. When the nurse is evaluating the labs of a patient with multiple myeloma, which finding would be expected?

    A. Proliferation of red blood cells
    B. Increased serum calcium
    C. Low number of circulating monoclonal proteins
    D. Decreased serum sodium

Rationale:

Correct answer: B

Myeloma is cancer of plasma cells within the bone marrow. The abnormal cells multiply rapidly, crowding out normal WBCs and RBS, leading to fatigue and inability to fight infections. The cancerous cells also produce abnormal antibodies, called *monoclonal proteins*, which can build up in the body and cause kidney damage. Patients with multiple myeloma will have increased serum calcium levels due to the destruction of bone marrow and subsequent release of calcium.

A is incorrect because patients with multiple myeloma tend to have a decreased number of red blood cells, leading to anemia and fatigue.

C is incorrect because increased monoclonal proteins are characteristic of multiple myeloma.

D is incorrect because sodium levels are not relevant to multiple myeloma. In cases where kidney damage is present, hypernatremia may occur as a result of the kidneys' inability to effectively excrete sodium and water from the circulation.

23. Hypercalcemia is an oncological emergency in patients with prostate cancer. Which of the following is a late sign of this condition?

    A. Thirst, sticky mucous membranes
    B. Seizures and increased neuromuscular irritability
    C. Diarrhea and dehydration
    D. EKG changes

Rationale:

Correct answer: D

Hypercalcemia is a calcium level greater than 10.2 mg/dL. This can cause a sedative effect on the central nervous system. Symptoms include muscle weakness, lack of coordination, decreased deep tendon reflexes, and EKG changes, such as cardiac dysrhythmias. When an excess of calcium is present in the bloodstream, the nurse may see a shortened ST segment and widened T wave.

A is incorrect because thirst and sticky mucous membranes are characteristic of hypernatremia, not hypercalcemia.

B is incorrect because seizures are a symptom of hypocalcemia, or total serum calcium less than 8.6 mg/dL.

C is incorrect because hypercalcemia will cause constipation.

24. The patient with squamous cell carcinoma is receiving intravenous bleomycin. The nurse expects which test to be ordered?

    A. Pulmonary function studies
    B. Lumbar puncture
    C. Renal computed tomography
    D. Abdominal radiography

Rationale:

Correct answer: A

Bleomycin is an antineoplastic antitumor antibiotic medication used to treat many cancers, including Hodgkin's disease, non-Hodgkin's lymphoma, and leukemia. Serious adverse reactions include pulmonary fibrosis and heart failure. Therefore, the patient's pulmonary function should be closely monitored.

B is incorrect because a lumbar puncture (LP) is not needed for a patient receiving bleomycin. An LP is a needle inserted into the subarachnoid space to inject medication or obtain a CSF specimen.

C is incorrect because bleomycin does not have an adverse reaction on the kidneys.

D is incorrect because abdominal radiography will not give any specific information about potential adverse effects of bleomycin.

25. The oncology patient is receiving megestrol acetate. The nurse should question this order if what medical history is noted in the patient's record?

    A. Asthma since the age of five
    B. Gout with chronic joint pain and swelling
    C. Thrombophlebitis in left leg after previous surgery
    D. Recent weight loss and cachexia

Rationale:

Correct answer: C

Megestrol acetate is a hormonal antineoplastic agent used to treat breast, prostate, and endometrial cancers. Because this medication suppresses luteinizing hormone, cases of thrombophlebitis can be worse. The physician should be notified to address the appropriate course of action.

A is incorrect because asthma is not a contraindication for the use of megestrol acetate.

B is incorrect because the patient with gout can safely take megestrol acetate.

D is incorrect because megestrol acetate is actually beneficial for a patient who has been losing weight because it acts as an appetite stimulant and has been shown to help increase weight in cancer patients.

26. Upon entering the patient's room, the patient reports that her sealed radiation implant for cervical cancer has become dislodged and fallen out. Which of the following priority nursing actions should be performed first?

    A. Contact the radiation oncologist
    B. Document the dislodgment
    C. Encourage the client to lie still
    D. D. Retrieve the radioactive source with a long-handled pair of forceps and place in biohazard bucket

Rationale:

Correct answer: C

This patient may have lost the sealed radiation device in her bed, or it may still be inside of her vagina. To prevent skin irritation or other hazards, the nurse should ask the patient to lie still until the implant has been located and retrieved. Once retrieved, the nurse should place the device in a lead bucket, contact the radiation oncologist, and document the occurrence and actions taken.

A is incorrect because locating the implant and properly sealing it in a lead bucket are priority actions that must be taken prior to calling the oncologist or nuclear medical specialist.

B is incorrect because documentation is not priority ahead of actual patient care at the bedside.

D is incorrect because instructing the patient to lie still is the priority until the nurse has located the implant. Once located, the item should be retrieved with long-handled forceps and placed in a lead bucket. A biohazard bucket is made of plastic and will not contain radiation.

27. The nurse is reviewing labs from a patient diagnosed with leukemia. The nurse knows that this patient is at risk of spontaneous bleeding when the platelet count falls below:

    A. 50,000 cells/mm³
    B. 150,000 cells/mm³
    C. 100,000 cells/mm³
    D. 20,000 cells/mm³

Rationale:

Correct answer: D

Normal platelet (thrombocyte) count is 150,000-450,000/mm³. Patients are at risk for spontaneous bleeding when the platelet count falls below 20,000 cells/mm³.

A is incorrect because patients are at risk of general bleeding (not spontaneous) when the platelet count falls below 50,000 cells/mm³.

B is incorrect because this platelet count is at the low end of normal and the risk for bleeding is not increased.

C is incorrect because the risk for spontaneous bleeding is when platelets fall below 20,000 cells/mm³.

28. The pre-operative nurse is providing patient education to a female client scheduled to have a right total breast mastectomy and lymph node removal. Which of the following patient statements would require the nurse to provide further education?

    A. "I should keep my right arm elevated after surgery."
    B. "I shouldn't carry anything heavy with my right arm when I go home."
    C. "I should wear snug-fitting sleeves, especially on the right side, to prevent blood clot formation."
    D. "I need to remind health care professionals to take my blood pressure on my left side."

Rationale:

Correct answer: C

Tight-fitting clothing on the affected side can impede lymph drainage and adequate circulation to the surgical site. Rather, this patient should be encouraged to wear comfortable, loose-fitting clothing.

A is incorrect because it demonstrates understanding.

B is incorrect because the statement indicates that the patient understands the limitations after surgery.

D is incorrect because it is true that the patient must avoid blood pressure readings on the affected side after mastectomy.

29. The nurse is talking with a patient who has expressed that they are nervous about their family history of adenocarcinoma in the esophagus. Knowing the major risk factors involved with developing this disease, the nurse would instruct this patient to avoid or limit all of the following activities except:

    A. Smoking cigarettes
    B. Drinking alcohol
    C. Using antacids
    D. Chewing tobacco

Rationale:

Correct answer: C

Esophageal cancer is a malignancy in the esophageal mucosa. Antacids may reduce chronic acid reflux, preventing the development of an irritated esophagus. For those who suffer from acid reflux, taking a prescribed antacid may help.

A is incorrect because cigarette smoke can contribute to esophageal cancer and increases gastric acid production.

B is incorrect because it is a good nursing action to teach this patient to limit alcohol consumption to decrease the risk of esophageal cancer.

D is incorrect because and tobacco products increase the risk of many types of cancers.

30. While providing education to an oncology patient scheduled to start chemotherapy treatment, the nurse states that chemotherapy acts on rapidly dividing cells. Knowing this, the nurse would be correct in stating that which areas of the body are most likely to be affected?

    A. Spermatocytes, lining of the GI tract, and hair cells
    B. Skin cells, oocytes, and fat cells
    C. Fat cells, GI tract lining, and hair cells
    D. Alveoli of the lungs, taste buds, and cervical cells

Rationale:

Correct answer: A

Chemotherapy acts on rapidly dividing cells such as spermatocytes, cells which line the GI tract (from the mouth to the anus) and skin and hair cells.

B is incorrect because while skin cells do indeed divide rapidly, oocytes and fat cells do not divide as rapidly and are not as affected by chemotherapy.

C is incorrect because fat cells are not as affected by chemotherapy as other more rapidly dividing cells.

D is incorrect because lung alveoli, taste buds, and cervical cells do not divide rapidly and are not primary target cells of chemotherapy treatment.

31. The nurse assesses four male patients. Which of the following is most likely suffering from testicular cancer?

    A. 60-year-old whose mother used diethylstilbestrol during her pregnancy with him
    B. 18-year-old, complains of pain while ejaculating
    C. 38-year-old reporting that one testis has become significantly smaller than the other during the past the weeks
    D. 22-year-old, complains of painless swelling of one testis

Rationale:

Correct answer: D

Testicular cancer is the most common cancer in men ages 15 to 35 years. Symptoms include painless swelling with or without a lump palpated in one or both testes.

A is incorrect because this patient has one risk factor for testicular cancer, but no symptoms are described. Women used diethylstilbestrol (DES) during the 1950s and 1960s to prevent miscarriage. Male babies born to women who used DES are at higher risk of developing testicular cancer.

B is incorrect because painful ejaculation is not a sign of testicular cancer.

C is incorrect because unilateral testicular atrophy is not a sign of testicular cancer.

32. The patient with gastric cancer is scheduled to undergo a Billroth I procedure. The nurse explains to the patient that this procedure will include:

A. Removal of the entire stomach, attaching the esophagus to the jejunum or duodenum

B. Removal of the stomach with the instillation of a Koch pouch

C. Partial removal of the stomach with the remaining portion routed to the duodenum

D. Removal of parts of the stomach with a routing to the jejunum

Rationale:

Correct answer: C

A Billroth I procedure is a type of bariatric surgery, also known as a gastro-duodenostomy. This procedure is performed by removing part of the stomach and rerouting the remaining portion to the duodenum.

A is incorrect because the removal of the entire stomach with an attachment to the jejunum or duodenum is known as a total gastrectomy.

B is incorrect because a Billroth procedure does not remove the entire stomach (known as a total gastrectomy).

D is incorrect because a Billroth I procedure routes to the duodenum rather than the jejunum. This variation is known as a gastro-jejunostomy, or a Billroth II procedure.

33. The oncological nurse is educating the student nurse about the phases of chemotherapy. Which of the following statements by the student nurse indicates an understanding of the induction phase?

    A. "Induction is the phase which decreases the tumor burden after initial treatment."

    B. "The portion of chemotherapy which prevents further invasion by leukemic cells is known as induction."

    C. "Induction includes the maintenance period of preventing and controlling remission."

    D. "Induction is the phase which occurs before surgery or radiotherapy and attempts to reach full remission."

Rationale:

Correct answer: D

The first phase of chemotherapy is called "induction" and aims to reach total remission or loss of leukemic cells. The patient may remain in the hospital for four weeks as high doses of chemotherapy are infused before surgery or radiation is attempted.

A is incorrect because the phase that decreases tumor burden after the initial treatment is known as intensification or consolidation therapy.

B is incorrect because central nervous system prophylactic therapy is the portion of chemotherapy that prevents further invasion by leukemic cells.

C is incorrect because the maintenance phase is responsible for controlling remission.

34. The oncology nurse is caring for a patient undergoing chemotherapy. Which of the following assessments indicate that the patient is experiencing nadir?

   A. The patient complains that bone pain is at its most extreme
   B. Platelet count reaches its lowest point
   C. White blood cells count begins to rise
   D. Nausea increases and becomes difficult to control.

Rationale:

Correct answer: B

The nadir is a period of time in which bone marrow suppression is at its greatest. Red blood cells, white blood cells, and platelets will be at the lowest at nadir, which usually occurs about 10 days after initial treatment.

A is incorrect because pain during cancer treatment varies depending on the site of the invasion and the type of therapy being employed. There is no term used to generalize the lowest point of pain, as this can be subjective.

C is incorrect because during the nadir, mature white blood cells will be much lower than normal. Cells counts begin to climb after the nadir period and may reach normal levels within three to four weeks.

D is incorrect because there is no term for the point of greatest nausea. Like pain, nausea can be subjective.

35. A 13-year-old child is being seen by the oncology service to be assessed for potential Hodgkin's disease. Which of the following positive test results would confirm this diagnosis?

   A. Elevated BUN levels
   B. The presence of Epstein-Barr virus in the blood

C. Elevated immature white blood cells in the bone marrow

D. The presence of Reed-Sternberg cells in the lymph

Rationale:

Correct answer: D

Hodgkin's disease is a type of lymphoma (cancer of the lymph system). The presence of Reed-Sternberg cells in the lymph is an indication of Hodgkin's disease. Hodgkin's disease is much less common than Non-Hodgkin's lymphoma. Treatment depends on the type of lymph cells affected by the cancer and may include both chemotherapy and radiation.

A is incorrect because elevated BUN levels do not indicate Hodgkin's disease. High BUN can be an indication of dehydration, renal damage, heart failure, or as an adverse reaction to fluoroquinolone antibiotics.

B is incorrect because the presence of the Epstein-Barr Virus in the blood indicates infectious mononucleosis.

C is incorrect because elevated immature white blood cells in the bone marrow often indicate leukemia, not Hodgkin's disease.

36. Which of the following antineoplastic medications is appropriately labeled according to its classification?

    A. Doxorubicin, an alkylating agent
    B. Tamoxifen, a hormonal antineoplastic agent
    C. Chlorambucil, an antimetabolite antineoplastic
    D. Methotrexate, an antibiotic antineoplastic

Rationale:

Correct answer: B

Tamoxifen is a hormonal medication used to treat breast cancer. It competes with estrogen to bind with estrogen receptor sites on malignant cells.

A is incorrect because doxorubicin is an antibiotic, antitumor antineoplastic (which can cause red urine) and is used to treat many cancers, including Hodgkin's and non-Hodgkin's lymphomas.

C is incorrect because chlorambucil is an alkylating agent that can be used to treat leukemia and multiple myeloma.

D is incorrect because methotrexate is an antimetabolite antineoplastic which can treat acute lymphatic leukemia and other cancers (colon, breast, stomach, and pancreas) and can also be used to treat psoriasis.

37. The nurse is helping a client prepare for magnetic resonance imaging (MRI). Which of the following requires additional assessment by the nurse?

    A. The client is allergic to mercury
    B. The client is wearing a wedding band
    C. The client complains of claustrophobia
    D. The client has advanced Parkinson's disease

Rationale:

Correct answer: D

MRIs use magnets to develop detailed images of internal body structures. Patients with Parkinson's disease may experience tremors which can impede the ability to achieve a clear image during the scan. The nurse must assess the patient for tremors and other involuntary muscular movements and determine if pre-medication is required before the procedure.

A is incorrect because gadolinium does not contain mercury.

B is incorrect because the wedding band can be removed before the MRI, no further assessment is needed.

C is incorrect because anti-anxiety medications are often given in preparation for an MRI to reduce nervousness and help the patient relax and lie still.

38. A client with cancer is being evaluated for the possibility of metastasis. Which of the following sites are most likely to be targeted by cancer cells?

    A. Urinary tract
    B. Spleen
    C. Liver
    D. White blood cells

Rationale:

Correct answer: C

The liver is one of the most common sites of metastasis along with the lung, bone, brain, and lymph nodes.

A is incorrect because cancer metastasizes to the urinary tract less commonly than the liver.

B is incorrect because of the answer choices, the liver is the most likely place for metastasis.

D is incorrect because cancer is more likely to spread to the liver than to white blood cells.

39. The nurse is preparing a patient for radiation therapy for gastric cancer. When teaching the patient about adverse effects of radiation therapy, the nurse should prepare the patient for which effect that is expected to occur?

    A. Hair loss from the scalp
    B. Generalized skin blotches on the extremities and trunk
    C. Abdominal discomfort and nausea
    D. Thyroid cancer

Rationale:

Correct answer: C

Side effects from radiation are specific to the area being irradiated. When irradiating the abdomen, the patient is likely to expect abdominal discomfort, nausea, vomiting, and diarrhea.

A is incorrect because scalp hair loss may occur as a side effect of chemotherapy or radiation to the head region.

B is incorrect because radiation to the abdomen may cause skin blotches to the area being radiated (the abdomen or trunk), not the extremities.

D is incorrect because although thyroid cancer is a potential long-term effect of treatment for lymphoma, it is not expected with abdominal radiation.

40. When caring for four patients with cervical cancer, which of the following findings is most concerning to the nurse?

A. The patient reports she began sexual activity at age 15

B. The patient had an abortion at age 19

C. The patient is found to have unilateral leg edema

D. The patient receiving cisplatin complains of nausea

Rationale:

Correct answer: C

Swelling in one leg can be a sign that cervical cancer is progressing, and this may be an indication for pelvic exenteration, a procedure in which portions of the pelvis are surgically removed to prevent the spread of the cancer.

A is incorrect because early sexual activity is a risk factor for cervical cancer. This gives the nurse information about prior risk factors, but this is not immediately concerning regarding a patient who has already been diagnosed with cervical cancer.

B is incorrect because history of abortion does not pose a major concern for a patient diagnosed with cervical cancer.

D is incorrect because nausea is a common side effect with cisplatin, an alkylating agent commonly used to treat cervical cancer.

Made in the USA
Middletown, DE
25 August 2021